PENGUIN BOOKS

The Ivan Morris Puzzle Book

Ivan Morris has written widely on modern and ancient Japan and has translated numerous works from both classical and contemporary Japanese literature. In 1965 Professor Morris received the Duff Cooper Award for his book *The World of the Shining Prince* (in the Pelican list). In 1968 his translation of *The Pillow Book of Sei Shōnagon* (a Penguin Classic), won exceptionally high praise on both sides of the Atlantic and also received the annual prize that the Japan Society of Translators awards for the best translation of a Japanese work of literature. He has recently edited *Madly Singing in the Mountains*, an appreciation and anthology of Arthur Waley. At present he is Professor of Japanese and Chairman of the Department of East Asian Languages and Cultures at Columbia University in New York.

THE
Ivan Morris
Puzzle Book

IVAN MORRIS

ILLUSTRATED BY
HUGH CASSON

PENGUIN BOOKS

Penguin Books Ltd, Harmondsworth,
Middlesex, England
Penguin Books Australia Ltd, Ringwood,
Victoria, Australia

First published in two volumes as
The Pillow-Book Puzzles and
The Lonely Monk and Other Puzzles
by The Bodley Head Ltd, 1969, 1970
Published in Penguin Books, 1972

Made and printed in Great Britain by
Richard Clay (The Chaucer Press) Ltd,
Bungay, Suffolk
Set in Monotype Baskerville

THE PILLOW-BOOK PUZZLES

Contents

Preface

In a world full of important puzzles whose answers are ambiguous, inconclusive, and often non-existent I have enjoyed testing my wits on these gratuitous ones, which have definite (and rather unimportant) solutions. Most of them I have picked up over the years from friends and acquaintances, starting with The Two Abyssinians (No. 9), which I heard during my days in preparatory school, when everything from conjugating Latin verbs to scoring cricket games was something of a puzzle, until Trains (No. 25), which was offered to me in its basic form the other day and to which, after much profound thought, I triumphantly produced an incorrect answer.

As I accumulated a small stock of these brain-twisters, I began exchanging them for new ones, rather like swapping stamps. Thus in return for the problem about the tortoise and the hare (No. 10) which was passed down to me via my Greek teacher from Zeno of Elea I acquired the schoolboy favourites about the family portrait (No. 31) and the irresistible force (No. 44); and these eventually led to even richer treasures like No. 12 about the three job-hunting professors (surely an invention of the hungry thirties) and No. 27, a useful little money-maker of Chinese origin, which was much played in the BBC newsroom when I worked there.

Often I have changed and I hope improved the wording and content of the puzzles. For example I transformed the precocious schoolboy who originally dominated No. 46 into a condemned prisoner, thus emphasizing the momentous potentialities of puzzle-solving; the anonymous shadows in No. 1 were materialized as well-known public figures; and the rather impersonal billiard balls that used to figure in No. 5 became, after promotion, an impressive squadron of fat women.

More recently I have taken to inventing my own puzzles (Nos. 2, 7, 36, 37, and 45 are among the harvest from this summer's labour) and have scattered them among the existing set. It is not a pastime that I would recommend to most friends; for it conduces to insomnia at night and in the daytime to spells of absent-mindedness, sometimes verging on a state of coma. On the other hand, the solution and invention of puzzles (one activity frequently leads to the other) can be a valuable tonic. Lewis Carroll, who used to spend many of his wakeful hours at night doing puzzles, wrote:

There are sceptical thoughts, which seem for the moment to uproot the firmest faith: there are blasphemous thoughts, which dart unbidden into the most reverent souls; there are unholy thoughts, which torture, with their hateful presence, the fancy that would fain be pure. Against all these some real mental work is a most helpful ally.

None of the 'Pillow-Book' puzzles requires any technical knowledge or advanced mathematical skill; but they vary enormously in difficulty. Some like Matchsticks (No. 6) and Ear-rings (No. 23) can and should be polished off in a matter of minutes; others like The Road to Heaven (No. 1) and The Twelve-Fingered Indians (No. 36) may require weeks, even months, before they yield to the probing mind. The Spoils of Battle (No. 47), which was provided by an ingenious Japanese visitor, stayed with me for well over a year before I found the solution; the visitor having disappeared, I had no way of asking him to put me out of my misery.

It would have been possible to give the puzzles in order of increasing difficulty. After some hesitation I decided that a mixed arrangement was more appropriate. Some readers may, however, wish to know which puzzles belong to which category of complexity, so that they can, for instance, avoid wasting their time with easy ones. I have established three categories: Brief Diversions, Hard Nuts, and Herculeans. These can be taken to correspond to the three types of starred restaurants in the *Michelin Guide*, which are defined respectively as '*une bonne table dans sa catégorie*', '*table excellente, mérite un détour*', and '*une des meilleures tables de France, une des gloires de la cuisine française: vaut le voyage*'. I have accordingly marked the puzzles with stars as follows: * (Brief Diversions), ** (Hard Nuts), *** (Herculeans); and I hope that at least as many readers will agree with my assessments as French gastronomes do with the judgements of the Michelin inspectors.

For the easiest of the Brief Diversions I have given the length of time that I regard as par for the hole. In taking on the Hard Nuts and the Herculeans the best approach is not always a frontal assault but a series of probing movements from different sides, which allow one to discover the weak points in the enemy's defences. Often the final breakthrough will come unexpectedly, in the middle of a conversation, for instance, or when waking from a dream. And sometimes one's startled eyes will see the white flag being raised long after all hope of success has been abandoned; if one has learnt to live with one's puzzles, like a patient general who lives in constant awareness of his enemy, the brain will have been battering away all the time. Then all that remains is a brief mopping-up operation – a couple of simple mathematical equations or a verbal formulation of the winning idea. These breakthroughs are moments of keen satisfaction – a modest sort of satori in fact – and the reader is advised not to deprive himself of them by prematurely consulting the Solutions, which are intended as a check rather than as a guide or shortcut.

I am grateful to Michael Knibbs for checking the wording of the Solutions and for making several suggestions, which he has modestly described as 'quibbles'; John Train has also been most generous with his criticism, advice, and invention. Other friends, whose names appear here and there in this collection, have made valuable contributions. I am especially indebted to Sir Hugh Casson, whose line drawings will surely bring the characters in these puzzles to life for many readers. To me they are all extremely alive, since I have spent so much time with them. Indeed they have assumed an immortality that none of us is likely to enjoy. The missionaries and cannibals are for ever gathered by their river-bank, while the condemned prisoner ceaselessly confounds the Governor with his shrewd logic; Jock and his little wife never leave their weighing-scale; and for all eternity those twelve fat women will be standing by their capacious seesaw.

Ivan Morris

Autumn 1968

1

The Road to Heaven

* * *

Reaching a fork in the road where one way leads to Heaven and the other to Hell, you encounter three shadowy figures. One of them (Gandhi) always tells the truth, another (Goebbels) never tells the truth, and the third (de Gaulle) sometimes tells the truth. It is impossible to distinguish among the three figures.

You are allowed two questions of the type that can be answered 'yes' or 'no' to find out which way leads to Heaven. Both questions may be addressed to the same shadow or the two questions may be addressed to two different shadows.

2

Professor Senapa's Walk from Columbia

* *

At 1 p.m. Professor E. J. Senapa starts walking from Columbia University at the corner of 116th Street and Broadway. He goes downtown in a straight line at an average speed of one block a minute, being delayed for half a minute by traffic lights at the end of every fifth block from his starting-point. After a time he realizes that he has gone one-quarter of the way to his destination; exactly two blocks later he finds he has gone one-third of the way.

What is the exact time when he reaches his destination?

Supplementary: If he continues walking for ten minutes beyond his destination, how many blocks will he be from his starting-point at Columbia University?

3

Percy and His Parents

* *

In twelve and a half years Percy, who is now eleven, will have reached the *mezzo del cammin* and will be exactly half the age of his parents. When Percy was born, his father was twenty-one. How old was his mother at that time? And how old will she be when Percy is twice as old as his father is now?

4

Numbers

* *

(*a*) What mathematical quality have 64 and 96 got in common that is shared by no other integer between 1 and 100?

Supplementary: Which is the next number in the series?

(*b*) What property is common to 50, 65, and 85 but to no other number under 100? What is the next number in the series? (*Proposed by Michael Knibbs, Esq.*)

5

The Fat Women on the Seesaw
* * *

Twelve fat women are standing by a seesaw. They all weigh exactly the same, except for Bertha, who is either heavier or lighter than the other eleven. Any number can be seated on the seesaw at the same time.

Determine in three seesaw operations which of the women is Bertha and whether she is heavier or lighter than her companions. The seesaw will tilt in either of the two directions, depending on which side is heavier, or remain exactly in the middle if both sides are of equal weight.

Supplementaries: 1. (I am indebted to John Train, Esq., for this supplementary.) If it is possible to do this with twelve women in three operations, how many women can you do it with in six operations? 2. How many seesaw operations would be required to discover which of 1,000 women is heavier or lighter than the other 999 and whether she is (*a*) heavier or (*b*) lighter than the others?

6

Matchsticks

*

(a) Move three of these matches to make four equilateral triangles (all the matches are of equal length):

(*Time: 5 minutes*)

(b) Move two of these equal matches to make six squares:

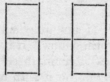

(*Time: 4 minutes*)

7

The Ballet Class

* *

The ballet mistress devises the following combination of movements for her class. Melinda and the twenty other dancers are told to stand in three parallel rows of seven girls each, the girls in the first row being numbered 1 to 7, those in the second row 8 to 14, and those in the third row 15 to 21. Then Melinda's row is told to move between the other two rows, unless of course it is already between them, in which case it stays there. The girls in the first row are renumbered 1 to 7, those in the second row 8 to 14, and those in the third row 15 to 21. Then the girls are told to dance gracefully into a new formation so that those now numbered 1, 4, 7, 10, 13, 16, and 19 form the first row, 2, 5, 8, etc., the second row, and 3, 6, 9, etc., the third row. Again Melinda's row moves into the middle position (unless it is already there). The girls are given new numbers (1–7 for the first row, 8–14 for the second, 15–21 for the third) and again they dance into a new formation so that those who now have Nos. 1, 4, 7, etc., form the first row, 2, 5, 8, etc., the second row, and 3, 6, 9, etc., the third row. Once more Melinda's row goes into the middle and the entire process is repeated. This continues for a few minutes. At the end of this time, what is Melinda's number? Why? Regardless of where Melinda was originally standing, what is the greatest number of times that the combination must be repeated before she reaches her final position?

Supplementary: If there had been altogether thirty-three girls, how many times would the pattern have to be repeated for Melinda to reach her final position and what would that position be?

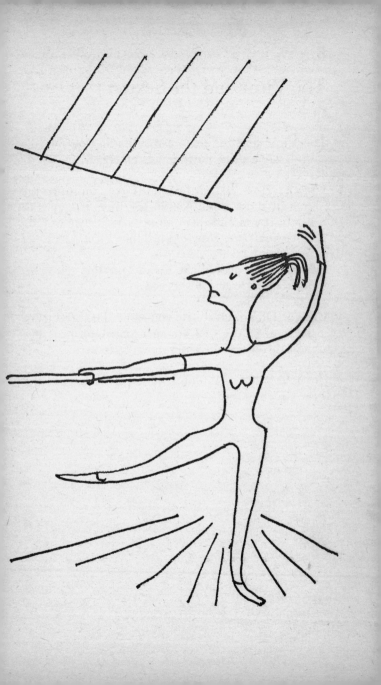

8

The Vicar and the Sexton
* *

The Vicar and the sexton are standing outside the church when three parishioners emerge.

VICAR: How extraordinary! If you multiply the ages of those three people together, it comes to 2,450. If you add them all up, it comes to exactly twice your age. How old are they?

SEXTON: My dear Vicar, I can't possibly tell without some further information.

VICAR: Oh no. Of course you can't. The product of the ages of the two younger parishioners is less than the age of the older one.

How old is the sexton and what are the ages of the three parishioners?

9

The Two Abyssinians

*

Two Abyssinians enter a bar; one Abyssinian is the father of the other Abyssinian's son.

How are they related?

(*Time: 30 seconds*)

10

The Hare and the Tortoise
* *

At the suggestion of Zeno, a hare challenges a tortoise to a 100-yard race. The hare, who can go ten times as fast as the tortoise, gives him a head start of ten yards.

'You will never catch up with me, let alone beat me,' claims the tortoise, much to the hare's amusement.

The race starts. By the time the hare has reached the point where the tortoise started, the tortoise has advanced one yard. By the time the hare has covered that one yard, the tortoise has gone a further one-tenth of a yard. When the hare has gone that one-tenth of a yard, the tortoise has advanced a further hundredth of a yard, etc., etc.

When, if ever, will the hare catch up with the tortoise? At this rate will it not take an infinite length of time?

Supplementary: When, if ever, will the hare catch up with the tortoise if the race was 300 yards, the handicap 13 yards, and the hare ran seven times as fast as the tortoise?

(*Zeno*)

11

The Headmaster's Dinner Party
* *

The headmaster and his wife are giving a dinner party. Altogether a dozen people are to be seated at the long rectangular table. Is it possible, and if so how, to place them in such a way that no two men and no two women will sit next to each other and that the Headmaster and his wife will be seated opposite each other at the far ends of the table with no guest sitting beside either of them?

Supplementary: How would it be possible to seat eighteen guests so that the Headmaster and his wife are at the far ends of the table with no one beside either of them, each male guest sits directly opposite one (and only one) female guest, and no two men or two women sit next to each other?

12

The Unemployed Professors

* *

Three professors of philosophy are seeking employment in a certain university. The Dean informs them as follows: 'I shall draw a blue or a white dot on each of your foreheads. If you see a white dot on anyone's forehead, please raise your right hand. As soon as you know your own colour, please lower your hand.'

He puts white dots on all three professors, and of course they all raise their hands. Fairly soon one of them, Professor Sol ('Ipy') Hoph, lowers his hand and declares, 'Obviously I must have a white dot.'

'How do you know?' asks the Dean.

Professor Hoph's explanation wins him the job. How does he explain that he must have a white dot? (There are no mirrors in the room.)

13

Roy and Marcia
* *

'I say, Roy!' exclaimed Marcia to her husband. 'Do you realize that my age is exactly twice what yours was when mine was twice what yours was when mine was three years more than yours was when mine was both three times what it was when you were born and three-quarters of your present age?'

'Of course I do,' replied Roy. 'And has it occurred to you how old I will be when your age is twice what mine will be when yours is the sum of both our present ages?'

'Yes, Roy, it has frequently occurred to me.'

'Very well. How old will I be?'

Marcia gives the correct answer. What is it?

14

Farmer Jones's Stone

* *

Farmer Jones's 40-lb millstone crashes to the ground and breaks into four integral pieces. To his delight the farmer discovers that with these four pieces he can weigh any amount of flour from 1 to 40 lb in integral pounds. How much does each piece weigh?

Supplementary: Into how many pieces would a 364-lb stone have to break for it to allow Farmer Jones to weigh any amount of flour from 1 to 364 lb?

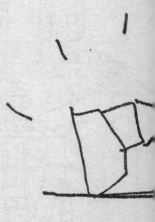

15

Prudence and Her Husband
*

Prudence is twenty-four. She is twice as old as her husband was when she was as old as her husband is now. How old is Prudence's husband?

(*Time: 6 minutes*)

16

(a) The Flying Saucers
*

1 All people who say they have seen flying saucers are liars.
2 No people who are free from delusions eat pork and strawberries for breakfast.
3 Granny Harris is honest.
4 No people who don't say they have seen flying saucers are given to delusions.

What final conclusion (i.e., conclusion that takes into account all the above information) can be drawn from these premises?

(b) The Student Problem
* *

1 No students who fail to put chocolate sauce on their oysters enjoy examinations.
2 Only students who love their professors consider studying classical Japanese literature.
3 All students with long hair listen simultaneously to Bach's 'B Minor Mass' and the Beatles.
4 All students who go to the cinema in the afternoons have been to prison.
5 Ismael Quinonez never spends illicit week-ends smoking marijuana.
6 All students who love their professors disapprove of violent demonstrations.
7 All students who don't consider studying classical Japanese literature wear long hair.
8 All students who have been in prison spend illicit week-ends smoking marijuana.
9 All students who disapprove of violent demonstrations enjoy examinations.
10 No students who fail to go to the cinema in the afternoons put chocolate sauce on their oysters.

What final conclusion, if any, can be deduced from these premises? The final conclusion should take all ten premises into account.

(c) People
* * *

1 No people fail to regard haiku as more expressive than sonnets unless they are particularly kind to small dogs.

2 Some people who don't regard haiku as more expressive than sonnets wear bowler hats and regimental ties.

3 All people who are not Japanese fail to regard haiku as more expressive than sonnets.

4 No one who is particularly kind to small dogs uses expressions like 'hopefully this will develop into a meaningful dialogue'.

5 No Japanese fail to regard bullfights and fox-hunting as equally repugnant.

6 All people who avoid expressions like 'hopefully this will develop into a meaningful dialogue' dislike stewed kidneys and tea for breakfast.

7 Some people who are particularly kind to small dogs are not very partial to the sound of a screaming baby.

8 People who regard fox-hunting and bullfights as equally repugnant don't prefer common sense to theory.

9 No Japanese spend much of their time reading the Court Circular in *The Times*.

10 Some writers of incredibly bad sonnets prefer common sense to theory.

11 No tall, blond brutes are Japanese.

12 Some people who are particularly kind to small dogs have no knowledge of art but can tell what paintings they like.

13 No one who writes incredibly bad sonnets is totally illiterate.
14 No one who regards haiku as more expressive than sonnets prefers a crowded cocktail bar to the wild enchantment of a windswept moor.

The aim is to find a final conclusion that takes into account as many of the above premises as possible.

(*Based on Lewis Carroll*)

17

Professor Mehta and His Indian Students

* *

Professor Tamic S. Mehta is standing outside the lecture hall where he has been lecturing a group of students. As the students leave the room at random, the Professor notes that the first five to emerge are all Indian. 'Interesting,' he remarks to his friend. 'The chances of that happening were exactly fifty-fifty.' How many students were in the lecture hall and how many of them were Indian?

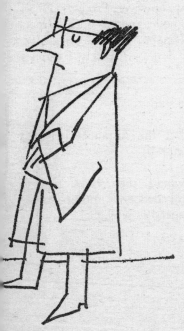

18

The Two Chess-Playing Professors on Riverside Drive

*

For many years Professor E. J. Senapa and Professor Sid Hews, who both live on Riverside Drive, have been meeting on Sundays for a friendly game of chess. They leave their respective buildings at three o'clock in the afternoon, walking towards each other at exactly the same speed and invariably meeting at 95th Street.

On one particular Sunday, however, Professor Hews is amazed to meet his colleague at 90th Street. 'You've been cheating, Senapa,' he says waggishly. 'Yes,' confesses Professor Senapa. 'Today I walked at twice my normal speed.'

What is Professor Senapa's address?

(It may be assumed that the distances between streets in New York are equal.)

Supplementary: Where would they have met if Professor Senapa had travelled on a motor-scooter at five times his normal speed of walking?

19

The Wettened Wrist-Watches
*

Roger and Mabel go for a swim, both forgetting to remove their wrist-watches. The watches are damaged. Roger's starts gaining thirty seconds a day and Mabel's stops entirely. If both of them decide never to set or repair their watches, which of the two will tell the exact time more often, and how much more often?

(*Based on Lewis Carroll*)

20

The Crushed Cyclist
*

Two motor-cars are 120 miles apart. One is travelling at 20 m.p.h., and the other is coming directly towards it at 10 m.p.h. A man on a motor-bicycle starting from the same point as the faster car and travelling at 30 m.p.h. goes to and fro between the two cars as they approach each other. How long does it take before he first reaches the slower car? How far has he travelled before he is finally crushed between the two cars?

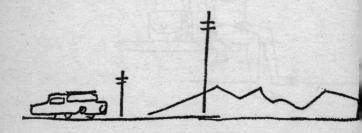

21

The Word Game
* *

What unusual feature do the following 6- and 7-letter words share apart from having 6 or 7 letters: tramps, craters, brandy, pirated, scampi, stores? What 8-letter word shares this feature?

22

Princes and Natives
*

There are three men in the room. You cannot see them, but you know that each is either a prince or a native and that princes always tell the truth while natives invariably lie. Each man is asked to identify himself in turn. Unfortunately the first person mumbles and you cannot hear what he says.

SECOND PERSON: 'The first person said he was a prince. He is, and I am one too.'

THIRD PERSON: 'I am a prince, but the other two aren't.'
What is the identity of each of the three men?

(*Time: 5 minutes*)

23

Ear-rings
*

There are eighteen similar silver ear-rings and eighteen similar gold ear-rings in a drawer. What is the minimum number of ear-rings that you must take out of the drawer (without looking) to make sure of having (*a*) one matching pair, (*b*) 9 pairs?

(*Time: 1 minute*)

24

The Match Trick
*

Ten matches lie in a row. Matches can jump over two other matches, moving either to the left or to the right, and then cross onto the third match. When a match jumps over a pair of crossed matches, it is equivalent to having jumped over two matches. Make five pairs of crossed matches in as few moves as possible.

25

Trains

* *

At precisely 2 p.m. on Monday the Los Angeles train left Chicago with Professor Tamic S. Mehta aboard. Trains were leaving Chicago for Los Angeles every hour on the hour and all were travelling at exactly the same speed. On the parallel line trains were also leaving Los Angeles for Chicago every hour on the hour and going at the same speed as the westbound trains. As he settled himself in his seat Professor Mehta noticed a Chicago-bound train pulling into the station from Los Angeles. Just then his own train started to move. 'Well,' remarked the Professor to his travelling companion, 'if we include that train and the one we shall see leaving Los Angeles at the moment we pull in, we shall be passing exactly sixty-one trains during the course of our journey.'

In how many hours will Professor Mehta and his friend arrive in Los Angeles?

(*Adapted from an invention by John Train, Esq.*)

Farmer Jones's Will

*

Farmer Jones on his deathbed divides his land as
shown in the illustration and says that the shaded
portion will go to the Church while the remainder
will be divided equally among his four sons. Draw
lines showing how an equitable division can be
made among the sons.

(*Time: 3 minutes*)

27

The Ancient Chinese Stick Game
* *

One possible arrangement in the ancient Chinese stick game is as follows:

I II III IIII IIIII IIIIII

According to the rules of this game, each of two players in turn removes as many sticks as he wishes from any single pile. The player who removes all but one of the sticks from the table wins. How many sticks should you remove from which pile in the above arrangement in order to win? Is victory certain however skilfully your opponent plays?

The Fat Man and His Doctor
* *

A man who is evidently suffering from obesity dis-
agrees (in a palindrome) with his doctor's view that
one way to avoid putting on weight is to eat less
food, and he refers to the ineffectiveness of his own
diet of cod: 'Doc, note, I dissent. A fast — — a
fatness. I diet on cod.' The two missing words contain 5 and 8 letters respectively. What are they?

(Suggested by James Michie, Esq.)

29

Odd Men Out

*

(a) Name the 'odd man out':
Nop Lad
Ileb Mug
Lay It
Bugar Lai
Soack Va Cehozil
Arn Fec

* *

(b) Which is the 'odd man out':
Mais
Nohl Lad
Raipes
Saf Moor
Nop Lad
Sauris
Inis Saaby
Rine Lad?

30

Jock and His Little Wife
* *

Jock, who weighs 200 lb, stands on a weighing-scale. He picks up his little wife, who weighs 100 lb, and makes her sit on his shoulders. The scale indicates 300 lb. A friend hands the wife a suitcase weighing 50 lb. The scale now indicates 350 lb. Jock is expending x units of energy to support the weight of the suitcase and y units of energy to support his wife's weight, i.e., a total of x plus y. The total amount of energy being expended by Jock and his wife is therefore x plus (x plus y) = $2x$ plus y. Jock's wife is weak and says she cannot hold the suitcase any longer. 'Give it to me, my dear,' says Jock. 'We'll be saving energy that way.' Jock's wife then transfers the suitcase to Jock. The scale still indicates 350 lb. Jock is still expending x plus y units of energy (for his wife and the suitcase). His wife, however, having relieved herself of the suitcase, is expending no energy whatsoever. The total amount of energy now being expended by Jock and his wife is therefore x plus y. What has happened to the additional x units of energy that were being expended before? Was Jock correct in saying that energy was being 'saved'?

31

The Family
*

(*a*) Pointing to one of the family portraits hanging
in the gallery, he remarked, 'Brother and sister
have I none, but that man's father is my father's
son.' How is the speaker related to the person in
the portrait?

(*Time: 1 minute*)

(*b*) Some moments later he continued in a plaintive
tone:
'Daughter, cousin, wife, half-sister –
They're all the same for this poor mister.'

How is this possible if there have been no
divorces in the family?

(*Time: 10 minutes*)

32

The Publisher, the Bookseller, and the Librarian
*

A publisher, a bookseller, and a librarian meet to talk in turn about their favourite books. To limit conversation they agree that, while each may speak

as often as he pleases, he will speak only half as long as the previous speaker. The publisher starts at 10 p.m. and speaks for exactly one hour. Why does the meeting end before midnight, and why is the publisher so unpopular?

(Suggested by Samuel S. Walker, Jr)

33

Anagrams
* *

(*a*) roast mule
(*b*) roast mules (*Produced by John Train, Esq.*)

Both are un-hyphenated, un-italicized words appearing in the dictionary.

34

Letters

*

Give the next member in these series:

(*a*) A E F H I K L
(*b*) B E J Q
(*c*) O T T F F S S

(*Time: 1 minute each*)

35

Jumbles

*

How many more single letters or combinations of letters can be made from the word RIDER than from the word RIDE?

36

The Twelve-Fingered Indians
* * *

Professor Charo A. O'Gleist discovers the following stone inscriptions in an ancient Indian site in South America:

1st inscription:
```
[•] [•]
[ ] [ ] [ ]
 •  [•]
```

2nd inscription:
```
            •
            •
        [ ] [•] [•]
```

3rd inscription:
```
 •
[ ] [•] [•]
```

4th inscription:
```
        •   •
       [ ] [ ]
        •  [•]
```

By external evidence Professor O'Gleist knows that the first three sets of symbols refer to the numbers of prisoners sacrificed after a series of famous battles and represent 836, 1,597, and 133 respectively.

Skeletal remains all indicate that this was a rather peculiar tribe of Indians who all had twelve fingers and toes instead of the usual number. How many prisoners were sacrificed after the fourth battle?

37

Judge Ling's Offer
*

'You have confessed,' said Judge Ling as the prisoner was removed from the rack, 'and now it is time for the sentence. You were stupid enough to commit a crime and to be convicted for it. Let us see how far your stupidity really goes. I shall allow you to choose your own sentence out of three possibilities – silver, bronze, and tin. One sentence is a fine of a hundred pounds of gold, another is a year in chains, another is slow strangulation. Remember that, according to our laws, if you do not promptly pay a fine, you are automatically sentenced to two years in chains. You do not know which sentence corresponds to which

metal, but within five minutes you may ask me two questions of the type that can be answered by a yes or a no. Then you must declare your choice, silver, bronze, or tin.' If you were the prisoner, what would be your questions?

(*Time: 5 minutes*)

38

The Professors and Their Birthday

* *

PLACE: the Senior Common Room

TIME: December 1968

PROFESSOR O'GLEIST: You're looking old today, Hoph. Did you sleep badly?

PROFESSOR HOPH: No, as a matter of fact I slept well. In any case, however old I may *look*, I shall always be 2,555 days younger than you.

O'GLEIST: Ah yes, you're quite right. (Pause) By the way, isn't it strange that we should both have been born on April Fool's Day?

HOPH: Not at all strange. After all, if there were twenty-three people in this room, the chances of two of them having the same birthday would be approximately even.

O'GLEIST: Yes, quite so. (Pause) And how many of them do you suppose would know that years followed by two noughts usually have only twenty-eight days in February?

HOPH: I expect that all our more educated colleagues would be aware of the fact.

How old are the two professors?

(Based on a puzzle suggested by Michael Knibbs, Esq.)

39

Dots

*

Connect these 9 dots by 4 continuous straight lines:

. . .

. . .

. . .

40

The Glass and the Olive

*

Move two matches in such a way that the olive ends up outside the Martini glass while the glass has exactly the same shape.

(Suggested by John de Cuevas, Esq.)

41

And
* *

(a) Give a complete, grammatical English sentence ending with the word 'and' (*not* in inverted commas as in: The last word in this sentence is 'and'). Try to reword the sentence so that it contains all the same information but does not end with 'and'.

and
*

(b) Give a complete, grammatical English sentence in which the word 'and' occurs three times in succession.

42

Prize-Day

* *

The headmaster is distributing the end-of-term prizes. The following books are to be awarded, one to each of the five boys who got the best marks: John Buchan's *The Adventures of Dickson McCunn*, Bulwer Lytton's *The Last Days of Pompeii*, Baroness Orczy's *The Triumph of the Scarlet Pimpernel*, F. E. Penny's *Love in the Hills*, and Rafael Sabatini's *Captain Blood*.

In a fit of absent-mindedness (he is actually more interested in the games cups) the Headmaster awards the books entirely at random instead of giving each one to the boy for whom it was intended. What are the chances that all five boys will nevertheless get the precise books they were supposed to be given? And what are the chances that exactly four of the boys will get the right books?

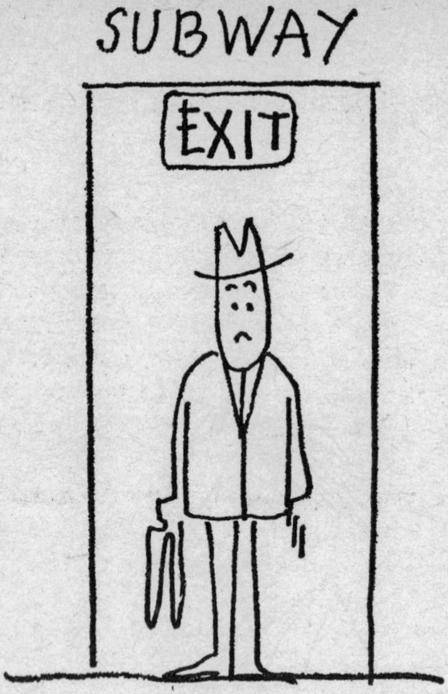
SUBWAY
EXIT

43

Brooklynites and Manhattanites
* *

Brooklynites all tell lies; Manhattanites all tell the truth. Having got hopelessly lost in the subway, you emerge on the street and see a passer-by. You know that he is either a Brooklynite or a Manhattanite, and you are allowed to ask him one short question (not more than four words) to find out where you are. What is the question?

(*Adapted from a suggestion by John de Cuevas, Esq.*)

44

Objects, Forces, and Distances

*

(*a*) What happens when an irresistible force meets an immovable object?

(*b*) How long would be required for an object travelling at the speed of light (186,000 miles per second) to cover an infinite number of miles minus 100 miles?

45

Bishop Stephen's Peaches
*

Bishop Stephen sent the Pope several boxes, each containing twenty peaches, and the following letter: 'I am sending Your Holiness several boxes of peaches, about two dozen boxes in all. The sum of the digits that compose the total number of the peaches is the number of the Holy Commandments.' How many peaches did the Pope receive?

46

The Condemned Prisoner

* *

PRISON GOVERNOR: I regret to inform you officially that you will be hanged during the course of this month, but you will never know in advance which day it is to be.

CONDEMNED PRISONER: Splendid! That means that I shall never be hanged.

PRISON GOVERNOR: Bother! So it does.

Was the prisoner's optimism justified? If so, why? And how should the Governor have worded his statement?

The Spoils of Battle
* * *

An ancient way of equitably dividing the spoils of battle (or anything else) between two people in such a way that neither had any justification for believing that he had received less than his fair share was for A to make what he considered to be an equal division and then for B to choose which of the two shares he preferred. How can an equitable division of this kind be made (without, of course, drawing lots) when three people are involved? Each of the three must be satisfied that he has received at least one-third of the spoils.

48

Pints

*

With nothing but a three-pint and a five-pint container, how can you measure one pint of liquid? (There is an indefinite supply of liquid.)

(Drunken drivers' test; time: 90 seconds)

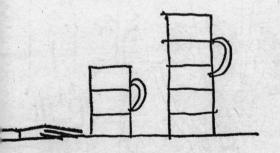

The Missionaries and the Cannibals
* *

'We had a terrible time getting across to the south bank of the river,' wrote Father Peter from the Congo. 'There were three of us missionaries, you see, and three of the natives, but the little boat would hold only two people at a time. We, of course, could

all row, but only one of the natives was capable of such skill. Also we had to remember that at no time could any of us missionaries be outnumbered by natives, or they would surely eat us. Even if we stayed in the boat after reaching the shore, we were in just as much danger of being eaten as if we had actually landed, for if the natives outnumbered us, they would drag us off the boat and eat us. However, we all managed to row safely across with the natives. How do you suppose we did it?'

50

International Date Line
*

If you travel from west to east, you gain a day each time that you cross the International Date Line in the Pacific. Thus, if it is 10 a.m. on Tuesday as you come to the Line, it immediately becomes 10 a.m. on Monday after you have crossed it. Since at present it takes at least 24 hours to go round the world by aeroplane, this gain is offset by the time spent in travelling. Soon, however, there may be supersonic aeroplanes that can circle the world in 12 hours. In a 24-hour period it will then be possible to go twice round the world and to cross the date line twice, thus saving two days against the expenditure of one day for travel, i.e., making a net gain of one day. Going at this speed, how many days would you gain if you travelled eastwards round the world for ten days? Why?

SOLUTIONS

Solutions

1

The real difficulty arises from the presence of someone who occasionally tells the truth, and the aim of the first question must be to 'eliminate' him so that the second question can be directed to a shadow that is known to be consistently honest or dishonest.

1st question: Let us call the three shadows A, B, and C. This question is directed to A: 'Is B more likely to tell the truth than C?' If the answer is 'Yes' then, if A is Gandhi, B is de Gaulle and C is Goebbels; if A is Goebbels, B is de Gaulle and C is Gandhi; if A is de Gaulle, B is either Gandhi or Goebbels, and C is either Gandhi or Goebbels. It will immediately be seen that in none of these three cases is C de Gaulle. Similarly, if the answer to the 1st question is 'No', then in none of the three cases can B be de Gaulle. The second question is therefore addressed to C or B, depending on whether the answer to the first question was 'Yes' or 'No' respectively. You do not know whom you are addressing, but you can be certain that it is not de Gaulle.

2nd question: 'Would the shadow whose truth/lying habits are the exact opposite to yours say that the left-hand road leads to Heaven?' If the answer is 'Yes', we know that the right-hand road leads to Heaven. For, if you were addressing Gandhi, he would reply that his 'opposite', i.e., Goebbels, would say that the left-hand road leads to Heaven, whereas in fact, it is the right-hand road that goes there; alternatively, if you were addressing Goebbels, he would reply that his 'opposite', Gandhi, would say that the left-hand road leads to Heaven, whereas he knows very well that what Gandhi would actually reply is that it is the right-hand road. In other words, the answer is the same regardless of whom you are questioning. Similarly, if the reply is 'No', it means that the left-hand road leads to Heaven. (An alternative second question depends on the use of a double negative, as in 'If you were asked whether the left-hand road leads to Heaven, would you reply in the affirmative?' If the left-hand road does in fact lead to Heaven, both Gandhi and Goebbels will answer 'Yes' to this question; if it doesn't, they will both answer 'No'.)

2

Let x be the number of blocks between Columbia and Professor Senapa's destination. Then $\frac{x}{4} + 2 = \frac{x}{3}$ and $x = 24$.

In walking 24 blocks, he is delayed four times, i.e., for two minutes, by the traffic lights; he therefore reaches his destination (which must be on the corner of 92nd Street) at 1.26 p.m.

The answer to the supplementary question depends on whether or not Professor Senapa stops at his destination. If he stops and starts again after a rest, we have the following situation:

$$24\ 25\ 26\ 27\ 28\ 29\ 30\ 31\ 32\ 33\ 34$$
$$\text{XX} \qquad\qquad\quad \text{X}$$

In five minutes he walks from 24 to 29 and is delayed there by the traffic light for half a minute. After six minutes he is *half-way between 29 and 30. Four minutes later he is half-way between 33 and 34.*

If, on the other hand, he continues walking without any stop at his destination, it means that he has been stopped by traffic lights at blocks 5, 10, 15, and 20 and that he is stopped again at blocks 25 and 30 after passing his destination. During the ten minutes after passing block 24 (his destination) he therefore spends one minute waiting for the lights and nine minutes walking, and so he reaches the corner of block 33, i.e., half a block less than if he had stopped to rest at his destination.

3

Let y be the age of Percy's mother when Percy was born. Then $2(12\frac{1}{2} + 11) = \dfrac{(y + 23\frac{1}{2}) + (21 + 23\frac{1}{2})}{2}$

$47 = \dfrac{y + 47 + 21}{2}$ *and* $y = 26$.

Percy's father is now 32. So in 53 years Percy will be twice his father's present age. Since his mother was 26 when Percy was born, she is now 37; in 53 years she will be 90.

Check: *In $12\frac{1}{2}$ years Percy will be $23\frac{1}{2}$, his father will be $44\frac{1}{2}$, and his mother will be $49\frac{1}{2}$. His parents' average age will be 47 and he will be exactly half that age:* mezzo del cammin.

4

(a) These are the only two numbers under 100 that have more than five factors, i.e., $2 \times 2 \times 2 \times 2 \times 2 \times 2$ and $2 \times 2 \times 2 \times 2 \times 2 \times 3$. The next number in the series is $2 \times 2 \times 2 \times 2 \times 2 \times 4 = 128$.

(*b*) *They are all the sums of two different sets of squares* (*i.e.,* *1–7 and 5–5, 4–7 and 1–8, 6–7 and 2–9*). *The next in the series is* *145*, *which is the sum of both 64–81 and 1–144.*

5

Let us designate the twelve fat women by numbers from *1* *to* *12*. **A B C** *and* **a b c**, *below, designate the situations that exist after the 2nd and 3rd weighing operations. The solution is based on two knacks* (*vid. inf.*).

> 1st operation: *women 1–4 on the left of the seesaw*
> *women 5–8 on the right of the seesaw*

If **A** *the seesaw balances,*
> 2nd operation: *9, 10 on the left*
> *11, 1 on the right*

(*N.B. We know that woman No. 1 is 'neutral', i.e., she is neither heavier nor lighter than the other 11: 1st knack.*)

If **a** *the seesaw balances,*
> 3rd operation: *12 on the left*
> *1 on the right*

Now, if the seesaw swings to the left, 12 is Bertha and heavy
> *if the seesaw swings to the right, 12 is Bertha and light*

If **b** *the seesaw swings to the left,*
> 3rd operation: *9 on the left*
> *10 on the right*

Now, if the seesaw balances, 11 is Bertha and light
> *if the seesaw swings to the left, 9 is Bertha and heavy*
> *if the seesaw swings to the right, 10 is Bertha and heavy*

If **c** *the seesaw swings to the right,*
   3rd operation: *9 on the left*
                  10 on the right

Now, if the seesaw balances, 11 is Bertha and heavy
      if the seesaw swings to the left, 10 is Bertha and light
      if the seesaw swings to the right, 9 is Bertha and light

If **B** *the* seesaw swings to the left, *we know that, if Bertha is among 1–4, she is heavy and that, if she is among 5–8, she is light: 2nd knack.*

   2nd operation: *1, 2, 5, 6 on the left*
                  3, 7, 9, 10 on the right

If **a** *the seesaw balances,*
   3rd operation: *4 on the left*
                  9 on the right

Now, if the seesaw balances, 8 is Bertha and light
      if the seesaw swings to the left, 4 is Bertha and heavy

If **b** *the seesaw swings to the left,*
   3rd operation: *1, 7 on the left*
                  9, 10 on the right

Now, if the seesaw balances, 2 is Bertha and heavy
      if the seesaw swings to the left, 1 is Bertha and heavy
      if the seesaw swings to the right, 7 is Bertha and light

If **c** *the seesaw swings to the right,*
   3rd operation: *3, 5 on the left*
                  9, 10 on the right

Now, if the seesaw balances, 6 is Bertha and light
      if the seesaw swings to the left, 3 is Bertha and heavy
      if the seesaw swings to the right, 5 is Bertha and light

If **C** the seesaw swings to the right, *we know that, if Bertha is among 1–4, she is light and that, if she is among 5–8, she is heavy (cf. 2nd knack above).*

Operations **C** *and* **Ca**, **Cb**, *and* **Cc** *are identical with* **B** *and* **Ba**, **Bb**, *and* **Bc**, *but in each case the results have the opposite significance in terms of 'heavy' and 'light'. If, for example, the result of* **Bb** *is that 7 is Bertha and light, the equivalent result of* **Cb** *is that 7 is Bertha and heavy.*

This is not the only solution, but all solutions are based on the two knacks identified above. The efficacy of any solution can be checked by making sure that provision is made for all 24 possibilities, i.e., that Bertha is either heavier or lighter than the other women. In the above solution the 24 possibilities are provided for as follows:

Bertha is			
1	and heavy	**Bb**	left
1	light	**Cb**	left
2	heavy	**Bb**	balances
2	light	**Cb**	balances
3	heavy	**Bc**	left
3	light	**Cc**	left
4	heavy	**Ba**	left
4	light	**Ca**	left
5	heavy	**Ca**	right
5	light	**Bc**	right
6	heavy	**Cc**	balances
6	light	**Bc**	balances
7	heavy	**Cb**	right
7	light	**Bb**	right
8	heavy	**Ca**	balances
8	light	**Ba**	balances
9	heavy	**Ab**	left
9	light	**Ac**	right

10	heavy	**Ab**	right
10	light	**Ac**	left
11	heavy	**Ac**	balances
11	light	**Ab**	balances
12	heavy	**Aa**	left
12	light	**Aa**	right

Thus, if Bertha should be woman No. 5, and if she should be lighter than all the other eleven women, the three weighing operations will result in **Bc** *right, which means that on the 1st operation the seesaw will swing to the left, on the 2nd operation it will swing to the right, and on the 3rd operation it will again swing to the right.*

Supplementaries: *This weighing system depends on having three groups of four women each. If four operations were allowed, three groups of twelve women each (i.e., a total of 36 women) could be weighed in the same way. The 1st seesaw operation would then be 12–12. If they balanced, we would have twelve women to weigh in three operations as in the original puzzle; if the seesaw swung to the left, the 2nd operation would be*

1, 2, 3, 4, 9, 10, 11, 12 on the left
5, 6, 13, 14, 25, 26, 27, 28 on the right, etc., etc.

In five operations, three groups of thirty-six women each (i.e., a total of 108 women) could be weighed. So the series is $3 \times 4 \ldots 3 \times 12 \ldots 3 \times 36$, etc., in other words, $3^1 \times 4$: for 3 operations; $3^2 \times 4$: for 4 operations; $3^3 \times 4$: for 5 operations, etc.

The formula therefore is $3^{x-2} \times 4$ where x is the number of operations. So in six operations we can weigh $3^4 \times 4$ women $= 81 \times 4$ women $= 324$ women. The 1st operation would be to put 108 women on each side. An unusually

97

large seesaw is required. Conversely, to discover how many weighing operations are required to determine which of a given number of women is heavier or lighter than the others and whether she is in fact heavier or lighter, the total number of women is divided by 4 and the power, or the next highest power, in the series 3^1, 3^2, 3^3, etc., is $(x - 2)$ where x is the number of operations. Thus, we divide 1,000 by 4 and get 250. The next highest number above 250 in the series $3 \ldots 9 \ldots 27 \ldots 81$ is 324, which is 3^5. So $x - 2 = 5$ and x (the total number of operations required) $= 7$. In the first operation we would of course put 324 women on each side of the seesaw.

6

(a) *The three bottom matches are stood on end to make a tetrahedron whose apex is directly above the centre of the triangle formed by the three top matches.*

(b) *The top and right-hand sides of the upper right-hand square are moved into the top and bottom positions in the centre of the diagram.*

7

By the nature of the combination Melinda is bound to end up in the centre of the centre row, i.e., as No. 11. Wherever she was standing originally, no more than three repetitions are needed for her to reach this central position, and once she is there she will stay in that position as long as the pattern is repeated. Thus, if Melinda's position was originally No. 6, this is how she would move to the central position in three stages (the girls are denoted throughout by their original numbers):

original		1	2	3	4	5	[6]	7
		8	9	10	11	12	13	14
		15	16	17	18	19	20	21
1st		8	11	14	3	[6]	16	19
		9	12	1	4	7	17	20
		10	13	2	5	15	18	21
2nd		9	4	20	14	16	13	15
		12	7	8	3	19	2	18
		1	17	11	[6]	10	5	21
3rd		9	14	15	11	5	7	19
		4	16	1	[6]	21	8	2
		20	13	17	10	12	3	18

Supplementary: *If there had been thirty-three girls (i.e., 3 rows of 11) the pattern might have to be repeated four times for Melinda to reach her final central position, No. 17. Here again, complete symmetry applies: if Melinda was originally in position Nos. 1 or 11, the pattern would have to be repeated four times; if she was in position No. 2, 3, 4, 8, 9, or 10, it would have to be repeated three times; for positions Nos. 5 and 7 there would be two repetitions, and for position No. 6 only one.*

8

There are eight plausible combinations of ages whose product is 2,450:

2	25	49	(total: 76)
5	14	35	(total: 54)
5	10	49	(total: 64)
7	14	25	(total: 46)
7	10	35	(total: 52)

2	35	35	(total: 72)
7	7	50	(total: 64)
5	7	70	(total: 82)

Since the sexton obviously knows his own age, he would immediately be able to tell which combination applies (e.g., if he is 41 years old, it must be the 5–7–70 combination), unless there are two or more different combinations that add up to twice his age. There are in fact two combinations that add up to the same total: 5–10–49 and 7–7–50. He therefore needs an extra clue and from this clue he learns that the 7–7–50 combination is the one to which the Vicar referred (since 7 times 7 is less than 50). Thus from the sexton's statement we know that his age is 32; from the Vicar's supplementary information we know that the ages of the three parishioners are 7, 7, and 50.

9

Husband and wife. It would also work with Americans, but not with people who are, e.g., English or French.

10

The analysis in paragraph 3 is entirely correct but the conclusion is of course false. By regarding the race as a series of isolated jerks in each of which the hare catches up with the tortoise who by then has advanced one-tenth of the previous distance between them, rather than as a continuous movement towards the finishing line, you make the distances smaller and smaller and the time of each movement shorter and shorter until the two animals are virtually not moving at all. What matters is the actual distances covered in a given number of minutes by the two bodies moving at different speeds, not the ever-decreasing amounts of time it takes to cover a series of ever-decreasing distances.

If the hare runs x yards in a minute, then the tortoise goes $\frac{x}{10}$ yards in a minute. If the tortoise has a start of 10 yards, let the hare catch up with him in y minutes:

$$xy = 10 + \frac{xy}{10}$$

$$and\ y = \frac{100}{9x}$$

In other words, the time it takes for the hare to catch up with the tortoise is the product of the tortoise's handicap and the number of times that he runs slower than the hare, divided by the product of the number of yards the hare runs in a minute and one less than the number of times that the hare runs faster than the tortoise.

So, if the hare runs 10 yards in a minute, x = 10 and the hare will catch up with the tortoise in $\frac{100}{90}$ minutes = $1\frac{1}{9}$ minutes.

Check: *In $1\frac{1}{9}$ minutes the hare will have run $11\frac{1}{9}$ yards. In the same time the tortoise will have gone $1\frac{1}{9}$ yards and, since he had a 10 yards handicap, he will be $11\frac{1}{9}$ yards from the starting line.*

Supplementary: $y = \dfrac{13 \times 7}{6\ times\ the\ hare's\ speed.}$

E.g., *if the hare ran 7 yards in a minute, he would catch*

up with the tortoise in 2 minutes and 10 seconds, at which time they would both be $15\frac{1}{6}$ *yards from the starting line.*

11

The basic rule of placement *is that* $\dfrac{x-2}{2}$ *must be an even number (where x is the total number of people at the table). If there are a dozen people,* $\dfrac{x-2}{2} = 5$ *and the normal seating is impossible. So long as the numbers on each side of the table are even, however, it is possible to alternate men and women. This can be done in three ways: (i) 6–4, (ii) 8–2, (iii) 10–0. The normal arrangement of 5–5 would not allow the Headmaster and his wife to sit at the far ends of the table.*

Supplementary: *If there are eighteen guests, x = 20 and* $\dfrac{x-2}{2} = 9.$

The normal seating arrangement is therefore impossible; and, since men and women are to be paired opposite each other, the unbalanced type of seating shown in the answer to the main part of this puzzle is not permissible.

12

Let us call the other two professors A and B. Professor Hoph reasons as follows: 'Suppose my dot is blue. Then Professor A must instantly realize that he is white (else why would Professor B be raising his hand?). Since Professor A has not in fact lowered his hand, my supposition must be incorrect. I am therefore white.'

The following solution is also possible (Knibbs): 'Assuming that a professor of philosophy would allow himself to go through the tomfoolery involved, he might also take for granted that all candidates were being tested in the same way. Therefore, if the other two have white dots and he did not, they were being given another test. Therefore he has a white dot.'

13

Her husband will be sixty.

Let a be Marcia's age, b Roy's present age, and x the difference between their ages. Then x = a minus b. Working backwards in Marcia's original statement, and designating the years to which she refers in the successive 'when' clauses as Year A ('when mine was both three times . . .'), Year B ('when mine was three years more . . .'), and Year C ('when mine was twice what yours . . .'), we get the following information from her statement:

In Year A Marcia was 3x and also $\frac{3b}{4}$. Since $3x = \frac{3b}{4}$ and $x = a - b$, we know that 5b = 4a.
In Year A, since Marcia was 3x, Roy was 2x.

In Year B Marcia was 2x + 3
*   Roy was (2x + 3) − x = x + 3.*

In Year C Marcia was 2x + 6
*   Roy was x + 6*

Since Marcia's present age is exactly twice this, a = 2(x + 6). Combining this with our knowledge that 5b = 4a and that x = a − b, we discover that a = 20, b = 16, and x = 4.

Check: *In Year A Marcia was 12 and Roy 8; in Year B*

Marcia was 11 and Roy 7; in Year C Marcia was 14 and Roy 10. And 2 × 10 = 20, which is Marcia's present age.

Working backwards in Roy's statement, and designating the two years to which he refers as Year D ('when yours is the sum . . .') and Year E ('when your age is twice . . .'), we find the following:

In Year D Marcia will be 20 + 16 = 36: Roy will be 32. In Year E Marcia will be 2 × 32 = 64: Roy will therefore be 60.

14

1 . . . 3 . . . 9 . . . 27 is the series. The best way to discover this is to start with light stones (3, 4, 5 lb, etc.), calculating how, if broken into two pieces, they can be used to weigh any amount up to their total weights. It will be found that a 4-lb stone broken into two pieces of 1 and 3 lb respectively can be used to weigh 1, 2, 3 and 4 lb (1, 3 − 1, 3, 3 + 1), but that a 5-lb stone broken into two pieces cannot be used to weigh 1, 2, 3, 4 and 5 lb. Similarly, a 13-lb stone broken into three pieces (1, 3 and 9 lb) can be used to weigh anything up to 13 lb (1, 3 − 1, 3, 3 + 1, 9 − 3 − 1, 9 − 3, 9 − 3 + 1, 9 − 1, 9, 9 + 1, 9 + 3 − 1, 9 + 3, 9 + 3 + 1), but a 14-lb stone broken into three cannot be used to weigh anything up to 14 lb. In the series 1 . . . 3 . . . 9 . . . 27 the effective stones are 4 lb (1 + 3), 13 lb (1 + 3 + 9), 40 lb (1 + 3 + 9 + 27), 121 lb (1 + 3 + 9 + 27 + 81), 364 lb (1 + 3 + 9 + 27 + 81 + 243), 1,093 lb (1 + 3 + 9 + 27 + 81 + 243 + 729), etc. The answer to the supplementary question is therefore 6 (and the weights would be 1, 3, 9, 27, 81, and 243 lb).

15

If her husband is x years old and if y is the difference between their ages, then $24 = 2(x - y)$; $y = 24 - x$.

So, $24 = 2x - 2y = 2x - 2(24 - x) = 2x - 48 + 2x$
$4x = 72$

Her husband is eighteen years old.

16

(a) *These 4 premises are part of a sorites. The conclusion can be found by combining any pair of premises (a–b) that have terms in common and drawing a result (z) from that combination; this result is in turn combined with another premise (c) with which it shares a term and a new result (y) is deduced; y is then combined with the final premise (d) and this will produce the final conclusion.*

The chain will invariably lead to the same conclusion regardless of which premise is taken first.

In the Flying Saucers premises 1 and 3 have a term in common, namely 'liar' and 'honest' (i.e., non-liar); we therefore combine these two premises as follows:

All people who say they have seen flying saucers are liars; Granny Harris is honest. Therefore Granny Harris does not say that she has seen flying saucers.

This result is then combined with premise 4 since they have a term in common (viz., 'don't say that they have seen flying saucers'):

Granny Harris does not say that she has seen flying saucers; no people who don't say they have seen flying saucers are given to delusions. Therefore Granny Harris is not given to delusions.

Finally this result is combined with the remaining premise, No. 2:

Granny Harris is not given to delusions; no people who are free from delusions eat pork and strawberries for breakfast. Therefore Granny Harris does not eat pork and strawberries for breakfast. (This is the final conclusion.)

(b) These 10 premises are part of a sorites, and the final conclusion is found in exactly the same way as with *The Flying Saucers*.

Premises 1 and 10 combine to produce:

Students who enjoy exams don't go to the cinema in the afternoons.

This combines with 9 to produce:

All students who disapprove of violent demonstrations go to the cinema in the afternoons.

This combines with 4 to produce:

All students who disapprove of violent demonstrations have been to prison.

This combines with 6 to produce:

All students who love their professors have been to prison.

This combines with 2 to produce:

No students who have not been to prison consider studying classical Japanese literature.

This combines with 7 to produce:

No students who have not been to prison fail to wear long hair.

This combines with 3 to produce:

No students who have not been to prison fail to listen simultaneously to Bach's 'B Minor Mass' and the Beatles.

This combines with 8 to produce:

No students who fail to listen simultaneously to Bach's 'B Minor Mass' and the Beatles fail to spend illicit week-ends smoking marijuana.

This combines with 5 to produce:

Ismael Quinonez listens simultaneously to Bach's 'B Minor Mass' and the Beatles. (This, and this alone, is the final conclusion.)

(c) Many conclusions can be drawn by using different combinations of premises. The following uses the largest possible number of premises, a total of eight:

Premises 4 and 6 combine to produce:

No one who is particularly kind to small dogs likes stewed kidneys and tea for breakfast.

This combines with 1 to produce:

No one who likes stewed kidneys and tea for breakfast fails to regard haiku as more expressive than sonnets.

This combines with 3 to produce:

All non-Japanese people fail to enjoy stewed kidneys and tea for breakfast.

This combines with 5 to produce:

No one who enjoys stewed kidneys and tea for breakfast fails to regard bullfights and fox-hunting as equally repugnant.

This combines with 8 to produce:

No one who likes stewed kidneys and tea for breakfast prefers common sense to theory.

This combines with 10 to produce:

Some writers of bad sonnets don't like stewed kidneys and tea for breakfast.

This finally combines with 13 to produce:

Some people who are not totally illiterate don't like stewed kidneys and tea for breakfast.

17

There are x students of whom y are Indian. The probability that five Indians will walk out of the room before any others is therefore: $y(y-1)(y-2)(y-3)(y-4)$: $x(x-1)(x-2)x-3)(x-4)$

So, since the chances were exactly fifty-fifty,

$$\frac{y(y-1)(y-2)(y-3)(y-4)}{x(x-1)(x-2)(x-3)(x-4)} = \frac{1}{2}:$$
$$x(x-1)(x-2)(x-3)(x-4) =$$
$$2y(y-1)(y-2)(y-3)(y-4)$$

Therefore, x = 10 and y = 9 (because 10 × 9 × 8 × 7 × 6 = 2 × 9 × 8 × 7 × 6 × 5)

So there were 10 students in the lecture hall and 9 were Indian.

Check: *The chances that the first student to leave the room would be an Indian were* $\frac{9}{10}$, *that the second student would be an Indian* $\frac{8}{9}$, *the third* $\frac{7}{8}$, *the fourth* $\frac{6}{7}$, *and the fifth* $\frac{5}{6}$; *cumulatively, the chances that the first five students would all be Indians were* $\frac{9 \times 8 \times 7 \times 6 \times 5}{10 \times 9 \times 8 \times 7 \times 6} = \frac{1}{2}$

18

Let x be the number of blocks that the two professors must walk to reach 95th Street. From Professor Hews's remark it is clear that Professor Senapa lives in a street with a higher number (i.e., farther north or uptown). Therefore Professor Senapa lives at 95 + x Street and Professor Hews at 95 − x Street. From Professor Senapa's confession we know that twice the distance between where Hews lives and 90th Street is equal to the distance between Senapa's building and 90th Street. Therefore $2[90 - (95 - x)] = 95 + x - 90$ and $x = 15$.

So Professors Senapa and Hews live in 110th and 80th Streets respectively.

Supplementary: *On a motor-scooter Professor Senapa would travel five times the distance that Professor Hews covers on foot, in other words, five-sixths of the total distance. Since the total distance is 30 blocks, Senapa travels 25 blocks and the meeting takes place at 85th Street.*

19

It will take $2 \times 60 \times 12$ half-days, i.e., 720 days, for Roger's watch to show the exact time again. During these days Mabel's watch will have shown the correct time twice every twenty-four hours, that is, 1,440 times. So her watch will have shown the exact time almost 1,500 times more often than Roger's.

20

It takes the motor-cyclist three hours to reach the slower car, by which time he has gone 90 miles and the car 30. The cars will collide in four hours, by which time the motor-cyclist will have travelled 120 miles.

21

Each of these words can be reduced to a one-letter word by removing the initial or terminal letters one by one in such a way that after each removal there is still a full word. E.g., pirated – pirate – irate – rate – ate – at – a. Among eight-

letter words with which this is possible are grangers, swingers, chastens, strowing. *James Michie, Esq., has produced the following nine-letter word:* prelatess, *and Michael Knibbs, Esq., is responsible for* aspirated. *I know of no ten-letter word in this category.*

22

The 8 possible combinations are:

$$P \quad P \quad P \quad N \quad P \quad N \quad N \quad N$$
$$P \quad P \quad N \quad P \quad N \quad P \quad N \quad N$$
$$P \quad N \quad P \quad P \quad N \quad N \quad P \quad N$$

P–P–N is the only one that works. In the case of N–N–P, which comes close to working, the first person is a native and his mumbling words were therefore 'I am a prince'; accordingly the second person, who is also a lying native, would not *have reported him as saying that he was a prince.*

23

(a) 3 ear-rings, (b) 19 ear-rings. It is always one more than double the number of pairs needed.

24

Let us number the matches 1 to 10 from the left; the matches change their numbers as they alter position.
(a) 4 goes left, (b) 6 goes right, (c) 7 goes left, (d) 3 goes right, (e) 10 goes left.

25

The easiest way to solve this puzzle is to reduce the time and the number of trains involved. If the journey took 2 hours, Professor Mehta would see the following east-bound trains:

(a) the train that left at noon and that was arriving in the station as he left, (b) the one that left at 1 p.m. (c) the one that left at 2 p.m., which would cross his own train at the half-way mark at exactly 3 p.m., (d) the one that left at 3 p.m., (e) the one that left at 4 p.m., which would be leaving just as his own train arrived at its destination. Similarly, if the journey took 4 hours, he would see 9 trains.

In other words, the formula is: time of the journey $= \dfrac{x - 1}{2}$

where x is the number of trains. In the puzzle as given the time required for Professor Mehta's journey is therefore $\dfrac{61 - 1}{2} = 30.$

Therefore Professor Mehta and his friend will reach Los Angeles in 30 hours.

26

		1	1
		2	1
4	2	2	3
4	4	3	3

27

The winner removes five sticks from the pile that has six sticks. This leaves the arrangement

I II III IIII IIIII I

which is absolutely invincible, as can be confirmed by a

binary breakdown of the numbers (1, 2, 1 + 2, 4, 1 + 4, 1). If, for example, the other player now removes the pile with two sticks entirely, the winner retaliates by removing two sticks from the pile that has three sticks, which leaves

❘ ❘ ❘❘❘❘ ❘❘❘❘❘ ❘

which is again invincible (the two one-piles cancel each other, and 4, 1 + 4, 1 obviously balance).

28

There are 20 letters before the missing words and 18 letters after. Reading the letters backwards, we get '-ts a fatness. I diet on cod'.

The 18 letters read backwards are 'Doc, note, I dissent. A fa-'

Clearly the second of the two missing words ends with -ts and it is almost certainly a verb with 7 letters in the infinitive form. The other word may well be an adverb. From the meaning of the sentence and the length of the words we arrive at 'never prevents' (-st never preven-).

29

(a) Poland, Belgium, Italy, Bulgaria, Czechoslovakia, France. Only Czechoslovakia is land-locked.

(b) Siam, Holland, Persia, Formosa, Poland, Russia, Abyssinia, Ireland. All except Poland have alternative names (viz., Thailand, Netherlands, Iran, Taiwan, Soviet Union, Ethiopia, Eire).

30

Nothing has 'happened' to the additional x units of energy.

Under the new suitcase-holding arrangement the two people involved are expending x units of energy less than under the original arrangement, and in this sense Jock's statement is correct. But there is no more reason to expect that the total expenditure of energy will remain the same regardless of the transfer of the suitcase from Jock's wife to Jock than there is to believe that, if a man lifts a 100-lb weight from the floor, the floor will then be supporting 100 lb less than it was before. I am indebted to Professor H. Webb for identifying the basic fallacy as follows: 'The formulation of the question involves an effort to apply to an artificially defined segment of the visible universe (i.e., the segment consisting of Jock, his wife, and the suitcase) the principle of the conservation or parity of energy, which in fact applies only to the universe as a whole.' (Cf. the fallacy involved in the formulation of the tortoise-and-hare puzzle, No. 10.)

31

(a) His father's son can be only himself. So he is in fact saying, 'That man's father is I', in other words, 'He is my son'.

(b) A married her cousin B and gave birth to the speaker; after B's death A lived with the speaker and by him had a daughter (C) whom the speaker married after A's death (their son being the man in the portrait). The speaker is therefore C's father, second cousin, husband, and half-brother.

32

It is mathematically impossible to continue until midnight in a sequence that will never reach 120 minutes: 60, 30, 15, 7·5, 3·75, 1·875, etc. The publisher (greedy rascal) speaks at least twice as long as the bookseller and at least four times as long as the librarian.

33

(*a*) emulators

(*b*) somersault

34

(*a*) M (all uncurved letters)

(*b*) Z (the order of these letters in the alphabet is 2 . . . 5 . . . 10 . . . 17; the next in the series is 26, which corresponds to Z)

(*c*) E (first letters of the words, one, two, three, etc.)

35

106 (170 minus 64)

Rider			Ride	
using 5 letters,	60 combinations			
,, 4 ,,	60 ,,		24 combinations	
,, 3 ,,	33 ,,		24 ,,	
,, 2 ,,	13 ,,		12 ,,	
,, 1 letter,	4 letters		4 letters	
	170 combinations or letters		64 combinations or letters	

36

If these Indians had twelve fingers and toes, there is good reason to suppose that they might have used some form of duodecimal system. In our own system of arithmetic, numbers are expressed by means of multiples of powers of 10, so that 365, for example, is $(3 \times 10^2) + (6 \times 10^1) + (5 \times 10^0)$. Here the multiples of powers of the basic number (10) are placed side by side with the higher powers placed progressively further to the left. Professor O'Gleist's Indians, on the other hand, evidently placed the multiples of powers of their basic number (12) on top of each other, in such a way that each row represents multiples of a different power of twelve, i.e., 1, 12, 144, 1,728, 19,736, etc. Let us examine the smallest number first: 133 (the 3rd inscription) can be broken down in the duodecimal system to $(11 \times 12^1) + (1 \times 12^0)$. This suggests (a) that the symbol ● represents 1, while □ ● ● combine to represent 11, (b) that the higher powers are written underneath the lower powers. The number 836 (the 1st inscription) can be analysed as follows: $(5 \times 12^2) + (9 \times 12^1) + (8 \times 12^0)$. Then ● ● combine to represent 8; □ □ □ combine to represent 9; and ● ● combine to represent 5.

Since we already know that ● represents 1, there is good reason to believe that ● represents $4(4 + 1 = 5;$ $4 \times 2 = 8)$ and that □ represents $3(3 \times 3 = 9)$. Let us now see if this checks with the remaining number, 1,597. If our assumption is correct, the first row must represent $1 \times 12^0 = 1$; the second row, $1 \times 12^1 = 12$; and the third row, $11 \times 12^2 = 1,584$. $1,584 + 12 + 1 = 1,597$. The working hypothesis is thus shown to be valid. In the 4th inscription we therefore have: $(2 \times 12^0)(= 2) + (6 \times 12^1) (= 72) + (5 \times 12^2) (= 720)$, making a total of 794.

37

If you had the gold, you would obviously prefer to pay the fine; otherwise you would prefer the year in chains. If you had the gold, your first question would be: 'Is silver the fine?' and, if the answer is negative, you would ask, 'Is bronze the fine?' Otherwise your questions would be, 'Is silver the imprisonment?' and 'Is bronze the imprisonment?'

38

In 1582 Pope Gregory XIII ordained that years ending in hundreds should not be leap years unless they were divisible by 400. The year 1900 was accordingly not a leap year (although the year 2000 will be one). Professors O'Gleist and Hoph were born on the same day of the year and the difference between their ages is precisely 7 × 365 (= 2,555) days. They must therefore have been born at the opposite ends of a span of time in which there were 7 consecutive years without a leap year. The only such span that would make it possible for them to be alive in 1968 is the one from 1896 to 1903. Professor O'Gleist is accordingly seventy-two and Hoph is sixty-five. (The rule of 23 is inserted gratuitously to help readers of these puzzles win bets. If there are 24 people in a room, the chances are better than even that two of them will share the same birthday.)

39

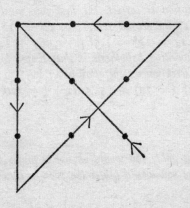

40

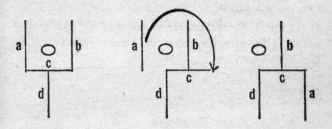

First move c to the right; then shift a so that it lies to the right of d and parallel to it.

41

(*a*) *Sarah is the girl I am sitting between the window and. Sarah is the girl who is sitting on the other side of me from the window.*

(*b*) *The pub sign has three words: 'Goat' and 'and' and 'Compass'.*

42

The number of possible combinations is the same as in a five-letter word, viz., $5 \times 4 \times 3 \times 2 \times 1 = 120$. The chances that all five boys will get the right books are therefore $\frac{1}{120}$.

The chances that precisely four boys will get the right books, however, are nil, since if four boys get the right books the fifth boy is also bound to get the book that was intended for him.

43

'*Do you live here?*'
*If you are in Manhattan, the answer will be '*Yes*' and, if you are in Brooklyn, the answer will be '*No*' regardless of the man's residence.*

44

(*a*) *An inconceivable disturbance.*

(*b*) *An inexpressible length of time; for it is impossible to subtract any finite number from infinity.*

45

If there were x boxes, the number of peaches was 20x. Since the digits that compose 20x add up to 10, the digits that compose x must add up to $\frac{10}{2} = 5$. The only number near 24 (two dozen) whose digits add up to 5 is 23. Therefore x = 23 and the number of peaches was 460.

46

The prisoner is entirely correct. According to the Governor's formula, the execution cannot possibly take place on the last day of the month; for, if the prisoner survives until the last day but one, he must know that only one day remains for the execution (namely, the last day) and the Governor has promised that he will never know the date of execution in advance. Since the last day of the month is thus ruled out, the last day but one is also impossible; for, if the prisoner lives through the last day but two, he must realize that the only day left for the execution (the last day having been eliminated as a possibility) is the last day but one, and again the Governor has said that he will never know in advance. Since the last two days of the month are disqualified, the last day but two is also disqualified by the same reasoning. Working backwards according to this logic the prisoner realizes that all the days of the month are ruled out.

Obviously the Governor should have added the following words to his original statement: 'unless, of course, it is the last day'. The prospect of being hanged, as Dr Johnson remarked, concentrates the mind wonderfully.

47

Let the people be A, B, and C. The important thing to remember is that all three may have different assessments of the value of the spoils and of any divisions thereof. First, A divides the spoils into three shares, Nos. 1, 2, and 3, which he considers to be absolutely equal. B is asked which of the three shares he wishes for himself and then C is asked the same question. If they choose different shares (e.g., Nos. 1 and 2), they are allowed to keep them, A is given the remaining share (No. 3), and everyone is content. If, however, B and C choose the same share (e.g., No. 1), they are asked to name their second choice. If their second choice is also the same (e.g., No. 2), A is given the share that neither B nor C wanted (i.e., No. 3), and B and C divide their first and second choices between them according to the ancient way of equitably dividing spoils between two people. If – and this is the most complicated situation – their second choice is different (e.g., B chooses No. 2 and C chooses No. 3), then B and C divide No. 1 equitably and keep this as part of their final share; B then divides No. 2 equitably with A, and C divides No. 3 equitably with A.

Check: *Let us suppose that A, B, and C assess the value of the shares in A's original divison as follows:*

Assessments of Value	No. 1	No. 2	No. 3	Total Assessment
A	40	40	40	120
B	90	30	10	130
C	130	90	100	320

In the above situation B and C divide No. 1 equitably and the result is: B = 45 or more: C = 65 or more.
A and B then divide No. 2 equitably and the result is: A = 20 or more: B = 15 or more.
A and C then divide No. 3 equitably and the result is: A = 20 or more: C = 50 or more.

When this is all finished, A considers that he has at least 40 (out of 120), B that he has at least 60 (out of 130), and C that he has at least 115 (out of 320). In other words, each of the three is satisfied that he has received at least one-third of the spoils. If the assessment is:

	No. 1	No. 2	No. 3	Total Assessment
A	80	80	80	240
B	18	10	3	31
C	35	23	21	79

A is given No. 3 entirely; B and C divide Nos 1–2 equitably. As a result A considers that he has 80, B that he has at least 14, and C that he has at least 29. Again each considers that he has received at least one-third of the spoils.

48

Fill the three-pint container; empty it into the five-pint container; fill the three-pint container again; empty it into the five-pint container until the latter is full; now one pint will remain in the three-pint container.

49

It required at least 13 operations as follows (M = missionary, C = non-rowing cannibal, C̲ = rowing cannibal):

1.	C̲ C	*crossed to the south bank*
2.	C̲	*crossed to the north bank*
3.	C̲ C	*crossed to the south bank*
4.	C̲	*crossed to the north bank*
5.	M M	*crossed to the south bank*
6.	M C	*crossed to the north bank*
7.	M C̲	*crossed to the south bank*
8.	M C̲	*crossed to the north bank*
9.	M M	*crossed to the south bank*
10.	C̲	*crossed to the north bank*
11.	C̲ C	*crossed to the south bank*
12.	C̲	*crossed to the north bank*
13.	C̲ C	*crossed to the south bank*

The easiest way to solve this is to work backwards. It will be found that in the final stage the rowing cannibal has to be on the south bank with the boat and the other two cannibals on the north bank. Operations 6, 7, and 8 are the real key to the solution.

50

You would not gain a single minute, because the gain made by crossing the date line is exactly offset by the loss made as you moved eastwards into progressively later time zones.

THE LONELY MONK
AND OTHER PUZZLES

Contents

Preface

Puzzles breed puzzles, and often the children out-shine their parents. Having recently put together all the best ones I knew (*The Pillow-Book Puzzles*), I never imagined that I would soon have an even richer supply in my larder; but so it is, and here they are.

This second helping comes mainly from ideas suggested to me by friends and correspondents who, having read my first puzzle book, realized I was an addict; others are variations on themes announced in the earlier collection; still others came to me completely out of the blue, usually when I woke up in the middle of the night.

Though I avoid puzzles that depend on special skills or knowledge, I could not resist the temptation to include one of Dawson's beautiful chess problems (a seemingly simple mate in two), and I have also used a couple of amusing, if slightly off-colour, French rebuses. The star system is the same as in my previous collection: * indicates Brief Diversion, ** Hard Nut, and *** Herculean. Readers are bound to disagree about my assessments (many of my Herculeans would no doubt be Brief Diversions for an Einstein), but I think they are useful as rough guides.

Bishop Stephen and young Percy have survived from my earlier cast, but all the other *dramatis personae* are new. Quite a few Japanese people have joined the ranks, possibly because I compiled the collection during a recent stay in Kyoto. Among them are Mr Tabako, an energetic, well-travelled businessman, typical of the New Japan, who loves both his racing-cars and his children, and Professor Baba, a distinguished academic gentleman who ekes out his modest salary with bets and lecture tours. Despite the vast difference in their styles of life, they are close friends and used to be neighbours.

Puzzles, I have found, admit no national boundaries: unlike humour, they are a sort of Esperanto of the mind. Even the best English joke or anecdote falls flat in Osaka, whereas a good puzzle is a truly international coin, giving equal pleasure to the happy few wherever they may be.

From the publication of my previous puzzle book I learnt that far more people enjoy these mystifications than I had supposed. Many acquaintances whom I would never have suspected of such tastes proved to be obdurate solvers. But reactions varied. The least enthusiastic was from a friend who confessed not only that he had failed to enjoy the puzzles but that the very sight of the book inspired him with nausea. Among the many judicious corrections that I received from a host of fellow-addicts scattered round the world from Glasgow to Hawaii was one about the two Abyssinians who enter a bar, one being the father of the other's son. In my answer to this Brief Diversion, which I learnt during my distant days in preparatory school, I naively stated that they were husband and wife. 'It is refreshing,' writes my learned correspondent, 'to find that there are still people who refer to a couple who have participated in the conception of a child as husband and wife. But the pedant must insist that the answer is incomplete.' O tempora! O mores!

Even the keenest puzzler is liable to dark moments when it occurs to him that there may be better ways to use his hours and wits than in trying to solve puzzles, let alone invent new ones. At such times of acedia it is well to remember the words of Dudeney, probably the greatest puzzle-maker of any age. He points out the practical value of these seemingly gratuitous efforts:

I do hold that the study of such crafty matters is good, not only for the pleasure that is created thereby, but because a man may never be sure that in some sudden and untoward difficulty that may beset him in passing through this life of ours such strange learning may not serve his ends greatly, and, mayhap, help him out of many difficulties.

Admittedly not all the situations in these puzzles are likely to occur as we pass through this life of ours: few of us will ever be obliged to distinguish between Finnish and Faroese fishermen, and fewer still will have to identify a pile of plutonium bombs on a station platform. But puzzles can have a value far more subtle and profound than the merely practical. Again it is Dudeney who has best expressed it:

Let these matters serve to call to mind the lesson that our fleeting life is rounded and beset with enigmas. Whence we came and whither we go be riddles, and albeit such as these we may never bring within our understanding, yet there be many others with which we and they that do come after us will ever strive for the answer. Whether success do attend or do not attend our labour, it is well that we make the attempt; for truly it is good and honourable to train the mind, and the wit, and the fancy of man, for out of such doth issue all manner of good in ways unforeseen for them that do come after us.

I have occasionally been asked what qualities are most important for solving puzzles. No doubt a modicum of intelligence is helpful; and for all but the most mechanical puzzles one needs a dash of imagination to lead one to the breakthrough. But not less important in my opinion is a combination of obstinacy and optimism which will provide one with the necessary determination to find the right path and buoyant confidence in following it. If one is convinced that the answer will be found, one is already half-way there.

Once again my thanks are due to Sir Hugh Casson for bringing the puzzles alive by his drawings. I am also most grateful to Dr Harry Hazard and Mr Lawrence Latto for all their valuable suggestions.

1

The Lonely Monk
* *

Father O'Sullivan, a young Zen monk, leaves his mountain hermitage at 5 a.m. and walks rapidly down the narrow path to the nearest village. He arrives before sunset and stays at a temple. After a few days he starts back up the mountain at 5 a.m., but since the path is steep and he is carrying a large box of pickled radishes his speed on the return journey is somewhat less than on the descent. He stops a couple of times for a short rest; at one of these stops he hears the distant booming of a temple bell and knows it will be dark by the time he reaches his hermitage. He also realizes that he passed this very point at exactly the same time of the day on his way down. As he continues trudging up the mountain it occurs to him with a flash of *satori*-like illumination that this was no mere coincidence but was bound to happen at some point on his way. Is he correct? And, if so, why? Or, if not, why not?

(*Based on an idea of Arthur Koestler's*)

2

The Chancellor and the Mafia
* * *

A hundred undergraduates are seated in the Assembly Hall. Ninety-nine of them are consistently honest or consistently dishonest, while one of them sometimes lies and sometimes tells the truth. The Chancellor, who knows this but has no idea which students tell the truth and which don't and which one equivocates, is allowed a total of two questions to discover whether the recent drug traffic in the university is under the control of the Mafia. All the students know the answer. What are the Chancellor's questions?

(*Adapted from a suggestion by Robert Cupples, Esq., Queen Margaret Hall, Glasgow*)

3

The Chess Players
* *

Jock MacKeetch, his sister, his son, and his daughter
all play chess. The best player's twin and the worst
player are of opposite sex; the best player and the
worst player are of the same age. Who plays the best
game of chess?

(*Offered by Michael Knibbs, Esq.*)

4

Mr Tabako's Motor-Car
*

Mr Tabako drives his Honda-Superspeed car round
a one-mile circular track at 30 m.p.h. At what speed
must he travel on his second lap in order to average
60 m.p.h. for the two laps?

(*Contributed by Professor Paul Varley*)

5

Pearls and Jars
* *

Mrs Tabako has fifty natural pearls, fifty cultured pearls, and two Ming jars. If she uses all the pearls, how should she distribute them in the two jars in such a way that when Mr Tabako enters the room and picks one pearl out of either jar at random he will have the best possible chance of picking a cultured pearl? What is the distribution and what are his chances?

(*Adapted from a puzzle posed by 'Doc' Hume*)

Supplementary: What distribution would produce the *least* possible chance of picking a cultured pearl?

6

Women

* * *

What conclusion can be drawn from the following six premises:

(*a*) all women who play the French horn before breakfast have a chance of becoming creative artists of no mean stature;

(*b*) Prunella van Blitz has a small waist and absurdly large breasts;

(*c*) no women who make sweet, docile wives drink alcoholic beverages;

(*d*) no women who are teetotallers fail to prefer smoking cigarettes to committing adultery in the afternoon;

(*e*) women who don't play the French horn before breakfast make sweet, docile wives;

(*f*) no women with small waists and absurdly large breasts prefer smoking cigarettes to committing adultery in the afternoon.

Prunella van Blitz

7

Black and Beautiful

* *

Prove that BLACK is not the square root of BEAUTIFUL.

(Algorithm invented by Dr Harry Hazard)

8

Jealous Husbands
* *

Three jealous husbands with their wives wish to cross a river at a ferry. They find a boat without a boatman, but the boat is so small that it can contain no more than two of them at once. How can these six people cross the river so that none of the women is left with any of the men unless her husband is present? Only three of the six people can row the boat, and men must row rather than women if a choice is possible.

(*Translated from* Problèmes plaisants et délectables *by Claude-Gaspar Bachet, Sieur de Méziriac, Lyons, 1612*)

9

Monkeys and Coconuts
* * *

There are five men and one monkey and a pile of
coconuts on a desert island. One man goes to the
pile of nuts, gives one to the monkey, removes a fifth
of the remaining nuts, buries them, and goes to sleep.
The second man then wakes up, goes to the pile of
coconuts, gives one to the monkey, buries a fifth of
what remains, and goes to sleep. The other men do
likewise. In due course all five men wake up and go
over to the pile of coconuts, which they then succeed
in sharing equally among them. What is the smallest
possible number of coconuts that the pile originally
contained?

(*Transmitted by Gillon Aitken, Esq.*)

Supplementary (*propounded by Martin Gardner, Esq.*): If
after the final division there is still one coconut
left for the monkey, what is the smallest possible
number in the original pile?

10

The Coloured Map

* *

Miss Tabako wishes to colour a sketch map of old
Japan which is divided into 68 provinces. She wants
to colour the map in such a way that no two neighbouring provinces have the same colour. Her father
gives her some crayons. 'But there aren't enough,'
she says. 'Oh yes, there are,' replies Mr Tabako.
'With these crayons you could colour a map with
any number of provinces without ever using the
same colour for two neighbouring provinces.' How
many crayons did he give her?

(*Based on an offering by Vercors*)

11

Pints and Tankards
* *

Gaston has ten litres of ale in his great cask; his two great tankards (5-litres and 3-litres) are empty. Using no other article, with no marking on any of the three vessels, and not wasting a single drop of ale, how does he put exactly one litre in each of his tankards? (Hint: drinking ale is not a waste.)

12

The Loved Ones
* *

'The loved ones', as they were called in the fashionable suburb where they all lived, consisted of the doctor and his wife, six other young married couples, three merry widows, twelve dashing bachelors, ten unmarried girls, and Percy Cod. In the course of a single month every member of this group except Mr Cod had sexual relations once with every other member, with the following exceptions and additions: there were no homosexual relations between the men; no married man had relations with any married woman except his own wife; all the bachelors made love to each of the unmarried girls exactly twice; the widows had no sexual relations with each other; and Percy Cod made love to no one. What was the total number of sexual relations among members of the group during the month?

(*Based on a puzzle by H. E. Dudeney, and inspired by John Updike's novel*, Couples)

Supplementary (*suggested by Dr Harry Hazard*): Which sub-group (e.g., bachelors, widows) had the highest *per capita* score, and how high was it?

13

Are Some Japanese People Unkind?
* * *

'Like so many Japanese these days,' said Professor Baba to his colleague, Professor Suzuki, 'you are quite a tall man, and tall people are inscrutable.' 'Yes,' said Suzuki. 'And generous people are always scrutable, aren't they?' 'Quite so,' replied Baba. 'And by the same token honest people are invariably generous ... By the way, I have recently decided that kind people are always honest.' 'I see,' said Suzuki. 'Then presumably we can conclude that there is such a thing as an unkind Japanese.'

Does Professor Suzuki's conclusion follow logically from the premises in this conversation? If not, what further premise is needed to justify it? And does his conclusion tell us anything about his own nature?

14

A Novelist at Work
* *

Frank Conroy, the author, is writing. His daily output is in proportion to the number of pages that remain to be written: the less that remains, the slower he goes. (According to the inner clock that determines Conroy's speed, a fraction of a page counts as a full page.) If page one takes him 10 days to write and the final page takes 50 days, how many pages are there in the volume and how long will it take him to finish?

(*Based on an idea suggested to me by Frank Conroy*)

15

On the Kyoto Super-Expressway
* *

Motoring along the super-expressway between Kyoto and Bingo, Mr Tabako sees exactly 100 cars coming in the opposite direction; they, and all the cars behind them, are travelling at the prescribed speed of 50 m.p.h. (as is Mr Tabako) and he sees them at equal intervals of time. If, instead of motoring to Bingo, Mr Tabako had parked his car at the entrance to the super-expressway in Kyoto without in any way affecting the Bingo–Kyoto traffic, how many cars would he have seen coming towards him along the expressway during the length of time it actually took him to reach Bingo?

(*Introduced by Mr Keiji Uenishi*)

16

A Lady of Fashion and Her Children

* *

A lady of fashion, who is sometimes described as belonging to the 'jet set', has six children, three girls and three boys. Their birthdays fall in only three months of the year, and they were all born in a period of almost exactly a dozen years. Each of the three birthday months contains the birthdays of a boy and a girl. If we divide the children into three pairs (eldest boy and girl, middle boy and girl, youngest boy and girl), we find that while only one of these pairs consists of children with birthdays exactly two years apart, nevertheless for half the year the ages of the children in the other two pairs, when given to the press (which the lady of fashion is naturally fond of doing), sound quite genuinely as if the boy and girl in each pair had been born at two-yearly intervals if you merely give the ages without the months, though in fact the intervals are greater. All four children in these two other pairs have birthday-months with the same initial letter. The youngest of the six children was born in February of a year whose second digit is the sum of the first and last digits and the same as the third digit read upside down. In what month and year was the second eldest child born?

(Adapted from an invention offered to me by Lady Antonia Fraser)

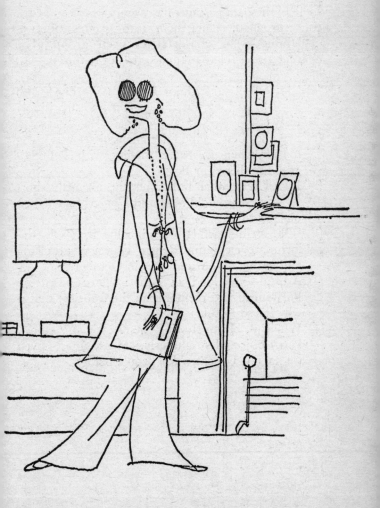

17

Food

* *

Each of these six passages has twenty words and each concerns food. Pair them into groups of two, explaining what characterizes each group. The characteristics relate to the words, not to the content.

(a) 'Bat soup,' said Major Hogg, 'is hardly a dish most of us long for, but in fact it's surprisingly tasty.'

(b) My very best recipe for cooking foxes was given to me when we were staying with Belinda's grandmother near Bognor.

(c) I well remember how after the absurdly short shooting season old Mac and I eagerly started on our pet rabbits.

(d) 'Oh, awful, awful!' exclaimed Alice. 'Oh, unfortunate elephants. Uncle Ernest is attacking and eating all our old ones in October.'

(e) Attitudes to food in America are based on Puritanism and memories of the frontier; that is why it's so awful.

(f) When we began stewing the electrician's elbow, Percy objected strenuously. 'Please desist. Even we have never eaten *live* people before.'

Bat soup

18

The Three Terrorists

* * *

Algernon, Basil, and Cyril have been arrested on suspicion of 'terrorist' activities and a Special Military Tribunal under General Crackblood has decreed that two of the three men will be shot on the following day. Until then each of them is kept in solitary confinement. Algernon has a chat with the gaoler, who knows which two of the men are to die. 'I realize that at least one of the two others is going to be executed,' says Algernon. 'Who is it? My own fate won't be changed in the slightest if you tell me whether it is Basil or Cyril who is going to die.' 'Not so,' replies the gaoler after some deep thought. 'If I were to inform you that Basil was definitely going to be shot, or alternatively that Cyril was doomed, your

chances of survival as you see them would improve considerably.' Who is correct, Algernon, or the gaoler, or neither? Why?

(*Provided by Professor S. Devons*)

Supplementary (*invented by Martin Gardner, Esq.*): Suppose that the gaoler in fact told Algernon that Basil was to die. Algernon has a secret way of communicating with Cyril by tapping on the wall of his cell, and he informs him that Basil is doomed and that they therefore both have a 50–50 chance of survival. If Cyril is a brilliant logician, what conclusion will he draw from the news about Basil?

19

Things

*

(a) What food appears more voluminous *after* a meal than before? (*Suggested by Nobuko Morris*)

(b) What vehicle normally moves independently and in a completely different direction within another moving vehicle? (*ibid.*)

(c) What creature can become at least a thousand times more valuable when ill than when in good health?

20

The Laetitia Riddle

*

> Laetitia has a large one
> And so has Cousin Luce;
> Eliza has a little one,
> But big enough for use.

Each child has a little one
Enclosed within a clout;
In fact all females have one –
No girls are born without.

Hermaphrodites have none;
Mermaids are minus, too;
Nell Gwyn possessed a double share,
If all we read be true.

Lasciviousness there has its source;
Harlots its use apply.
Without it lust has never been,
And even love would die.

'Tis known to all in nuptial bliss,
In carnal pleasure found.
Without it love becomes extinct –
The word is but a sound.

Now tell me what my object is,
But pause before you guess it;
If you be mother, mate, or man,
I swear you don't possess it.

21

The Barrel of Saké
*

Two brothers, Kichibei and Magoichi, own a little
inn on the old Great Eastern Highway. One day
they are returning to their inn with a barrel full of
saké. They have agreed not to drink any of the *saké*
themselves, since it is all intended for their cus-
tomers; but Kichibei becomes unbearably thirsty
and, taking a silver coin from his purse, offers it to
Magoichi in return for a large ladleful of *saké*.
Magoichi agrees to the sale. Seeing his brother drink,
he himself becomes thirsty and offers the same coin
in return for a similar drink. Once they have started,
they find it hard to stop, and the coin changes hands
time after time until the barrel is empty. Kichibei
is much dismayed, but Magoichi comforts him by
pointing out that they have had the pleasure of
drinking an entire barrel of *saké* for the price of a
single silver coin. Is Magoichi mistaken in believing
that this is a bargain? If so, why?

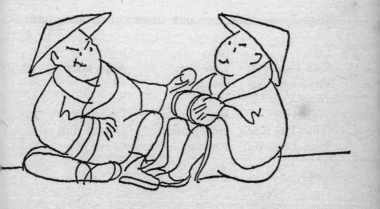

22

Fu Hsi's Eight Diagrams
* *

In the Eight Diagrams of Fu Hsi (*c.* 3000 B.C.) ☰
is equivalent to our 6, ☳ to our 1, and ☶ to
our 3. What does ☷ represent?

23

Odd Men Out
* *

Identify the 'odd men out' among these anagrams:

(a)	(b)	(c)
Rot Tin Lean	Tan doe	Taps mise
Pus Mire Vio	Get not	Ill nag
Limp Cab Cee	Ret ilk	Sef roe
Pint Ride	Rod are laid	Dec dens
Nine Tits Rang	Iron lented	O Ivan Pill
Posh Lean Biti	Ruse up	O rut pus

24

That, And, Had

* *

Give complete English sentences in which (*a*) the word 'that', (*b*) the word 'and' appear five times in succession, and (*c*) in which the word 'had' appears eleven times in succession.

25

A Dull Number

*

The British mathematician G. H. Hardy called on his friend Srinivara Ramanujan, the Indian mathematical genius, in a taxi with the number 1729. 'That is a dull number,' remarked Hardy. 'No,' replied Ramanujan immediately, 'it is a very interesting number. It is the smallest number expressible as the sum of two cubes in two different ways.' What are the two ways?

(*True story supplied by John Train, Esq.*)

Angus MacGregor and
Professor Baba

*

(*a*) Angus MacGregor's office is on the 35th floor
   of the Royal Insurance Company. Almost every
   morning he takes the lift to the the 25th floor and
   walks up the remaining ten flights of stairs; but
   in the evenings he travels all the way down in
   the lift from the 35th floor. Why? (Note:
   MacGregor has no need or desire for exercise.)

(*b*) Professor Baba is on one of his lecture tours in Kyushu. Late at night he telephones the room next to his in the hotel. A man answers.

'Is that Mr Tabako?' asks Baba.
'No,' says the man.

Professor Baba puts the telephone down and shortly afterwards (as a result of the telephone call) goes to sleep. Explain his behaviour in four simple words.

27

Three Bankers and Two Fishermen
* * *

(a) You are confronted with three bankers, one from
Albania, one from America, and one from
Austria. You do not know which is which, but
you do know that one always tells the truth, a
second always lies, and a third sometimes lies
and sometimes tells the truth. How many questions are needed to identify their respective
nationalities?

(*b*) **On** the following day you are confronted with two fishermen, one Finnish and one Faroese, one of whom always tells the truth while the other usually tells the truth but occasionally lies. How many questions do you need to determine their nationalities?

(*Based on variations by Professor Herschel Webb*)

28

A Beautiful Chess Problem

* * *

White to play and mate in two moves. Explain why there is one *and only one* solution.

(*T. R. Dawson invented this magnificent problem*)

29

Professor Suzuki's Children
* *

Professors Suzuki and Baba meet in the Dining Hall of Waseda University.

SUZUKI: Hullo. How are you this evening?

BABA: Splendid, thank you. And you?

SUZUKI: Very well. You know I have three children now.

BABA: Really? How old would they be?

SUZUKI: Well, you're good at mathematics and logic. You should be able to work it out. The product of their ages is 36 and the sum of their ages is the same as the number of that house in Osaka you used to live in.

BABA (after a pause): That is not enough information.

SUZUKI: Quite right. Well, the oldest one looks exactly like me.

BABA: Ah, now I can tell their ages.

How old are the three children?

(*Suggested by Barry Polsky, Esq.*)

30

Matches
*

(*a*) A dozen matches are arranged in the following
pattern:

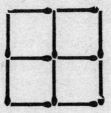

Move two of them in such a way that you produce
seven squares.

(*b*) Move three of these equal matches to make eight
equilateral triangles:

31

Neighbours and Utilities

*

Professor Baba, Mr Tabako, and Percy Cod used to be neighbours. How could you connect water, gas, and electricity to each of their three houses in such a way that none of the pipes crosses another at any point?

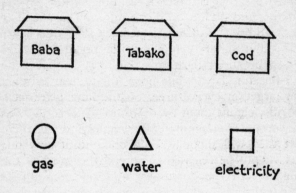

32

The Three Poachers and Their Punishment

* * *

A poacher is detected among the royal elephant herds and brought before the king, a sportsman who detests poachers. His Majesty recalls that he has held two earlier captives in his dungeons for several months, and decides to dispense rough justice. The latest addition, Casimir, is a crack shot who never misses, but solitary confinement on bread and water has so impaired Bertram's skill that he kills only half the time now, while poor Alfonso can kill only one target in every three. So the king gives each his rifle, chains them by the waist to three posts at the corners of an equilateral triangle, and tells them that they will shoot at each other until only one survives, to be released to spread the word of the king's severity, magnanimity, and sporting outlook. To equalize their chances, Alfonso is given first shot, then Bertram, and then the infallible Casimir, with subsequent rounds in the same rotation. If each follows his best strategy in choosing targets, what are the chances of each man to survive the ordeal?

(*Suggested by Dr Harry Hazard*)

Supplementary: If the king wished to equalize the survival chances of the three poachers by ordering that an equal number of blank cartridges, indistinguishable from the real ones, be mixed into one or more men's ammunition, how many such blank cartridges would be distributed and to whom?

33

Bishop Stephen's Nursery
*

and
* * *

Bishop Stephen buys a nursery of fruit trees en bloc.
It consists of a number of trees laid out in rows with
the same number of trees in each row as there are
rows. There are ten poor priests in his diocese and
he generously gives the same number of trees to each
priest. When the gifts have all been made, Bishop
Stephen discovers to his chagrin that only a single
tree is left for himself. All the priests plant the trees
they have received in square patterns. How many
trees did Bishop Stephen start with?

Supplementary: How many trees did the Bishop start
with if there were thirteen (instead of ten) poor priests
in the diocese?

(*Inspired by Michael Knibbs, Esq.*)

34

Professor Baba's Bet

* *

To eke out his meagre salary Professor Baba starts
offering bets as follows: 'I bet that at least two
people in this room have birthdays in the same
season.' How many people must be in the room for
Baba's chances of winning to be better than even?
(It may be assumed that the distribution of birthdays
is unaffected by the difference in the lengths of the
seasons, e.g., that just as many people are likely to
have been born in Spring as in Winter.)

35

Animal Words

*

In fifteen minutes write down as many words as
possible in the following category: cocky, mulish,
capricious, lousy. What quality, apart from being
related to animals and being used to describe human
beings, is shared by the overwhelming majority of
the adjectives?

36

The Scorpion
* *

A room is 30 feet long, 12 feet high, and 12 feet wide.
In the middle of the square side in the north of the
room, one foot under the ceiling, sits a large scorpion
which can only crawl but neither fly nor drop. For
some peculiar reason the scorpion wants to crawl the
shortest way to a spot which is one foot above the
floor in the middle of the opposite (i.e. the south)
side. How many feet is its shortest route?

(Received from Dr Walter Bergmann)

37

Casualties of War

* *

When visiting a field hospital shortly after an unsuccessful battle General Crackblood is told that precisely two-thirds of the men have lost an eye, three-quarters an arm, and four-fifths a leg. 'It follows,' says the General to his aide-de-camp, 'that at least twenty-six of these men must have lost all three

– an eye, an arm, and a leg.' If General Crackblood is correct (and he is), exactly how many men are in the hospital?

(*Based on an invention by H. E. Dudeney*)

38

The Bishop of Salisbury's Riddle
* * *

This is the famous Bishop of Salisbury's Riddle (also
known as Hallam's Enigma), but I have added the
last couplet in order to remove ambiguities:

I sit on the rock, and call for the wind,
But the storm once abated, I'm gentle and kind.
I have kings at my feet who await but my nod
To lie down in the dust on the ground where I've
   trod.
I'm oft seen in the world, though known to but
   few;
The Gentiles despise me, I'm pork to the Jew.
I never passed but one night in the dark
And that was with Noah alone in the Ark.
My weight is three pounds, my length is a mile
And when you have guessed me you'll say with a
   smile
That my first and my last is the boast of our Isle.

A mere nothing I am, yet without me, I vow,
You'll be dead in a trice – you'd be dead even now.

The answer is a word of one syllable.

39

Mechanical Beetles
*

Six mechanical beetles are arranged as follows:

The beetles can jump over each other or move straight forward; but they cannot go backwards, turn round, or move to either side. What is the smallest number of jumping or moving operations necessary for the beetles to end up in this position:

40

Missing Words
*

Supply the missing words in these palindromes:

(a) (question asked in the house of a famous poet in London): 'Was it – – – – – – toilet I saw?'
(b) (apocryphal remark by Henry Purcell): 'Egad, a base tone – – – – – – – a bad age.'
(c) (advertisement in *The Times Educational Supplement*): 'Note: Nine – – – – – open in Eton.'

41

The Vizier's Will

*

On his deathbed the Grand Vizier, who has two sons, announces that his entire fortune will go to the son whose horse loses a race in which the two of them must compete simultaneously. The sons, both keen horsemen, are accustomed to winning races but do not know how to lose them. Since in this case both are determined to lose, they do not see how such a race is possible, but a wise man explains how it can be managed. What simple method does he suggest?

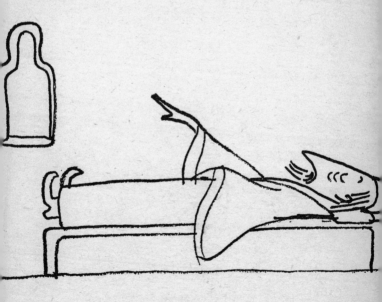

42

Jelly-Beans
* *

Mr Tabako comes home with a box of jelly-beans to be divided among his seven daughters, who are all of different ages. Each girl is to receive from the box the number of sweets by which her age can be divided into the total number of jelly-beans, and all the jelly-beans are to be distributed. Nonchan, who is the middle child if the children are listed in order of their ages, receives 18 jelly-beans. How many years older is she than the youngest girl?

(Based on an idea contributed by Gillon Aitken, Esq.)

43

English Rebus and French Rebuses
*

(*a*) English rebus:
   if the B mt put:
   if the B. putting:

* *

French rebuses (*provided by John Napper, Esq.*):

(*b*)

(*c*)   peu   tu   peu
          trop   tu   trop

44

Chess Clocks
*

Chess clocks have two faces; as soon as a player has completed his move he punches a button which stops his side of the clock and starts his opponent's side; and in this way it is possible at any moment to tell the total amount of time that each player has taken for all his moves. What would be the minimum number of such double-faced clocks required to determine the total time that each of four Scrabble players has taken for all his moves?

General Crackblood and the Courier

* *

A column of men is marching slowly forward at exactly one mile an hour. General Crackblood, who is at the rear of the column, tells the courier that he

has a message for the Colonel, who is at the head of the column ten miles away. 'I want you back here in exactly one hour,' he says, 'and I want you to go at an even pace both ways.' Assuming that no time is lost in actually delivering the message, at what speed should the courier set off? (It must be remembered that by the time the courier reaches the head of the column it will have moved ahead considerably from its present position.)

(Based on a puzzle posed by John Train, Esq.)

46

The Dishonest Porter

*

Mr Tabako and two business associates arrive at a
hotel in St Louis and pay $10 each (a total of $30)
for a room, which they intend to share. The manager
later decides that he has overcharged them (since
the lavatory is not working) and therefore gives $5
to the porter to return to the men. On his way up
to their room the porter pockets $2 and returns $1
to each of the men. Mr Tabako and his associates
have now paid $9 each (a total of $27); the porter
has $2. This makes a total of $29. What has happened to the remaining dollar?

47

A Number Circle and Two Number Series

* *

(*a*) What is the missing number in the following diagram (based on an advertisement by Aquascutum of London):

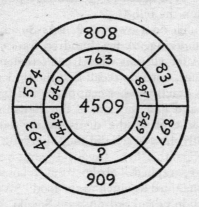

(*b*) What mathematical property is shared by 60, 65, and 95 but by no other number less than 100? What is the next number in the series?

(*Offered by E. J. Ulrich, Esq.*)

(*c*) What is the next number in this series:
$1^1 \ldots 2^2 \ldots 3^2 \ldots 4^2 \ldots 3^3 \ldots$?

48

First Night in Paris
* *

On their first night in Paris Mr Suzuki and Mr Tabako take their wives to an expensive dinner at La Pérouse. Unfortunately Mrs Kazuko Tabako is a teetotaller and Mrs Suzuki has a bad case of diarrhoea. The men agree to 'go Dutch', but Tabako actually pays the bill.

'How much do I owe you?' asks Suzuki on the following morning. 'A few hundred francs,' replies Tabako. 'After all that wine I can't remember the exact amount, but I do recall that the tip I gave the waiter was exactly 20 per cent of the bill (including the wine) and that the sum of the digits in my tip was 20 per cent of the digits in the bill itself.' 'Incidentally, how much did they charge us for that delicious Chambertin?' 'Again I can't recall the exact figure,' replied Tabako. 'But I know it cost precisely one third as much as the food.' 'Well, since your wife didn't drink a drop,' says Suzuki, 'I should pay twice as much for the wine as you do.' 'Fair enough,' says Tabako. 'But by the same token, since your wife didn't eat a morsel, I should pay twice as much for the food as you do.' 'Agreed,' says Suzuki, extracting his wallet. How much should he give Tabako for his share and his wife's?

Supplementary: Why is it usually easier to remember the amount of the tip than the amount of the actual bill?

49

Percy's Death

*

Percy, who comes from a remarkably vigorous family, was born in 1961, the very year in which his father died at the age of eighty. Until what age must Percy live if the year of his death is to share the remarkable property that both the year of his birth and the year of his father's birth have in common?

50

Vowels

*

(*a*) What English words contain the five vowels, a-e-i-o-u, once and once only in their alphabetical order?

* *

(*b*) What English words contain them once and once only in the reverse order?

51

A Variation of Nim
* * *

In a variation of Nim, the ancient Chinese stick game, each of two players in turn removes as many sticks as he wishes from either a single pile or two different piles. (He may, for example, remove all the sticks from two piles or just a single stick from one pile.) The player who takes all but one of the sticks from the table wins. How many sticks should you remove from which pile or piles in the following arrangement in order to win?

I   II   III   IIII   IIIII   IIIIII   IIIIIIII

52

The Professor's Dinner Party
* *

The Professor and his wife have invited ten people
to dinner, and they are to be seated at a long rectangular table. 'Strange!' remarks the Professor's
wife. 'Precisely half the people at the table will be
Japanese. Can you arrange them so that no Japanese
will be seated next to a non-Japanese (the language
difficulty, you know!), that you and I will be directly
opposite each other, that no two women will sit next
to each other, and that I shall have a Japanese on
one side of me but not on the other?' 'Certainly, my
dear,' replies the Professor. 'Nothing could be
simpler. I'll put you next to the Colonel, and I'll seat
old Professor Morris on my right.' Draw a chart
showing the *placement*.

53

The Sheik's Camels
* *

In his Last Will and Testament the Sheik says that anything not specifically bequeathed to a member of his family shall go to the Great Mosque. In the clause concerning his camels he makes the following provisions: 'My eldest son will get half my camels, my middle son will get one third, and my youngest son one ninth.'

Since there are seventeen camels, the sons do not know how to divide them without cutting one of the camels into pieces. While they are discussing the difficulty, a wise man (the same one as in number 41) appears on a camel. The sons ask him what they should do. 'Quite simple,' he says. 'Let us add my camel to yours. There are then eighteen camels, so the eldest of you will get nine, the second will get six, and the youngest two, which makes a total of seventeen, precisely the number that the Sheik left you.' The sons divide the seventeen camels accordingly, and the wise man rides off on his own camel. Is this arrangement satisfactory from everyone's point of view? If not, why not?

54

Many Numbers

* *

(*a*) addition. What does *money* come to in figures:

$$
\begin{array}{r}
\text{SEND} \\
+\text{MORE} \\
\hline
\text{MONEY}
\end{array}
$$

(*b*) multiplication. What is a:

$$
\begin{array}{r}
27 \\
\times \quad a \\
\hline
10b,000,000
\end{array}
$$

(*c*) multiplication. E = even, O = odd, and there are three possible solutions:

$$
\begin{array}{r}
\text{EEO} \\
\times \quad \text{OO} \\
\hline
\text{EOEO} \\
\text{EEO} \\
\hline
\text{OOOOO} \ (\text{product})
\end{array}
$$

55

Jock MacKeetch and His Wife
* *

Jock MacKeetch takes a train to arrive home at six o'clock every night; his wife meets him by car and drives him home. One night he was able to leave his office early and took the train an hour earlier than usual. He sent a message to his wife, but she did not get it. Seeing no one at the station, he started walking until he saw his wife coming to fetch him. She saw him and drove him home, and he arrived home twenty minutes earlier than usual. How long did he walk? (Mrs MacKeetch drives at a constant speed and no time was lost in picking her husband up and turning round.)

56

Gaston and the Beer

*

Many years ago during the famous monetary dispute
between Belgium and Luxembourg the Belgian franc
was worth only 90 centimes in Luxembourg and the
Luxembourg franc worth only 90 centimes in Belgium.
Gaston, a shrewd Belgian peasant, went into a beer-
hall in Luxembourg, bought a tankard of beer for 10
centimes, paid for it with a Luxembourg franc, and
requested his change in Belgian money. He received
one Belgian franc and returned to the Belgian side
of the border, where he visited a similar beer-hall,
bought beer for 10 centimes, and received one
Luxembourg franc in exchange after having tendered
his Belgian franc. He kept crossing and re-crossing
the border in this way all day long until he had
drunk as much beer as he could manage, and when
he finally returned to Belgium he still had a full
Belgian franc, which he had received in exchange
during his final visit to the beer-hall in Luxembourg.
Who paid for Gaston's beer?

57

February 1972
* *

February 1972 has five Tuesdays. When was the last
such February?

58

Arnold Toynbee's
Grandfather
*

'In my case,' writes Arnold Toynbee in *Man's
Concern with Death* (pp. 260–61), 'when I learned my
name, I learnt at the same time the reason why I
bore it. I learned that I had been called after an
uncle of mine who had died six years before I had
been born. I had been called after him because I had
been the first male child in my uncle's and father's
branch of the Toynbee family to be born after my
uncle's death . . . At the age of thirty [my uncle] had
died, already a famous man . . . On the day on which
I am reading these words in proof, I myself am
seventy-nine years and three months old . . . Both
my grandfathers had died prematurely and suddenly,
though my Toynbee grandfather had lived to be
twenty-one years older than his son Arnold was when
Arnold died twenty-two years later than his father.'

How many years before Arnold Toynbee read his
proofs was his grandfather born, and how many
years intervened between the grandfather's death and
the grandson's birth?

59

The Balloon
* *

Mr Tabako's little boy sits in the back seat of a
closed motor-car, holding a balloon on a string. All
the windows of the door are closed tight. The
balloon is full of coal gas and is tethered by the
string, which prevents it from touching the roof of
the car. The car turns left at a roundabout. Does
the balloon (a) swing left, (b) swing right, (c) stay
upright, (d) do something else? And why?

(*Given to me by Gerald Stonehill, Esq.*)

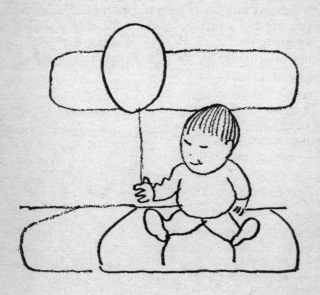

60

Bombs
* *

On a station platform lie eleven piles of bombs, each
pile consisting of exactly ten bombs. One pile consists entirely of miniature plutonium bombs, each
weighing one pound; all the other piles contain
only normal bombs, each weighing two pounds. All
the bombs look identical, but you are in a desperate
hurry to discover which are the plutonium bombs.
You cannot risk trusting your own judgement by
picking up the bombs and comparing their weights.
Fortunately there is an accurate weighing machine
on the platform; the attendant agrees that you may
weigh any number of the 110 bombs, but insists that
you use the weighing machine for only one single
weighing operation. How do you use the weighing
machine to identify the pile of plutonium bombs?

61

Nobel Prizes
*

On the occasion of receiving his second Nobel prize
Dr Linus Pauling, the chemist, remarked that, while
the chances of any person in the world receiving his
first Nobel prize were one in several billion (the
population of the world), the chances of receiving a
second Nobel prize were one in several hundred (the
total number of living people who had received the
prize in the past) and that therefore it was less
remarkable to receive one's second prize than one's
first. In sixty seconds and the simplest possible
language explain the fallacy (if any).

62

Transformations
*

These transformations are by Lewis Carroll. Here is
a simple example of how it is done: *cat* ... cot ...
cog ... *dog*. Now change the following:

(*a*) *hare* into *soup* in 7 steps,
(*b*) *black* into *white* in 8 steps,
(*c*) *army* into *navy* in 8 steps,
(*d*) *elm* into *oak* in 8 steps.

63

Longfellow's Bees
*

Henry Wadsworth Longfellow used to give this
pretty puzzle to students of literature: if one fifth of
a hive of bees flies to the ladamba flower, one third
to the slandbara, three times the difference of these
two numbers to an arbour, and one bee continues
to fly about, attracted on each side by the fragrant
ketaki and the malati, how many bees are there?

SOLUTIONS